D1591486

A
HERITAGE
IN WOOD

A HERITAGE IN Wood

The Chesapeake Bay Maritime Museum's Small Craft Collection

Richard J.S. Dodds
Pete Lesher
Editors

This publication has been financed in part with State Funds from the Maryland Historical Trust, an agency of the Department of Housing and Community Development of the State of Maryland. However, the contents and opinions do not necessarily reflect the views or policies of the Maryland Historical Trust or the Department of Housing and Community Development.

© 1992 Chesapeake Bay Maritime Museum
St. Michaels, Maryland 21663

Library of Congress Catalog Card Number: 91-073776

ISBN 0-922249-02-4

BOATS OF THE CHESAPEAKE

Bugeye and schooner and pungy and sloop.
Bateau and yawl and the old canoe –
Away with a song where the green shores loop
And the broad bay rolls in its tides of blue!

A skiff with her cat-rig, a wind off shore,
Dreams, and the drifting when dies the breeze;
Down again, home again, one leg more
To the gates of the capes of the wild, great seas!

Bugeye, the dainty, with slender waist,
Pointed ends and her slim, sharp keel,
Walking the waters by fair winds chased
With her taffrail down and her bare, brown heel;
Winged with wonder and light as spray,
A dancing beauty that soars and sweeps
To the golden beaches of yesterday,
        Where love in a garden of roses sleeps!

Pungy, bouncing and skipping along,
        And the sloop with her mainsail of snow a-wing;
The swift canoes o'er the waves of song,
Bound for the islands of youth and spring;
Schooners rolling in troughs of foam
        Lumber-laden or glowing green
With melon cargoes for ports of home
And the oyster fleet in the offing seen!

Boats on the Chesapeake – hoist, and away;
Up with the canvas, O hearts of dream.

The Cambridge Record, Historical and Industrial Edition, Albert E. Walker, ed. 1908.

To Josef W. Liener for his lifelong dedication to preserving America's wooden boat heritage.

CONTENTS

FLAT-BOTTOM BOATS   72

GUNNING BOATS   85

ONE-DESIGN BOATS   110

MISCELLANEOUS BOATS   122

LIST OF PLANS

The Chesapeake Bay Maritime Museum gratefully acknowledges the following individuals and organizations for permission to use their photographs:

Front Cover, Richard J. S. Dodds; p. 18, Vernon McNamara; p. 24, Jack Cane; p. 25, Mrs. Myrtle Messick; p. 30, top, Mrs. Nellie Poet; p. 39, Robert H. Burgess; p. 40, top, Larry Crew; p. 43, The Mariners' Museum; p. 44, Bethel Historical Society; p. 45, Library of Congress; p. 49, bottom, Jeremy W. North; p. 55, bottom, John G. Earle; p. 59, Clarence W. Strickland; p. 61, bottom, Elmer L. Ward, Jr.; p. 62, top, Hayden Photo Collection, Southern Maryland Room, Learning Resource Center, Charles County Community College, La Plata, Maryland; p. 65, Robert H. Burgess; p. 68, Robert H. Burgess; p. 70, Tom Parks; p. 71, John Frye; p. 74, Jack Cane; p. 75, right, Audrey F. Fletcher; p. 81, John G. Earle; p. 89, Enoch Pratt Library; p. 91, Jack Cane; p. 105, Pauline T. Pease; p. 106, right, Nelson H. McCall; p. 112, John Aldrich; p. 115, Historical Society of Talbot County; p. 116, John G. Earle; p. 118, Edward Coughlin; p. 119, Jack Cane; p. 123, John G. Earle.

"No other state in the Union has, in proportion to its area, a coastline so extensive as that of Maryland, and more persons are supported in Maryland by capturing and preparing the products of the water than in any other state."

Maryland – Its Resources, Industries and Institutions, 1893.

FOREWORD

Most Americans, wherever they live, are aware of the Chesapeake Bay – or should be. Those of us in Maryland, Virginia, and Delaware have had our awareness more finely tuned in recent years by the persistent acuteness of its ecological decline. It is good that we still have this great body of water living at all. But this is not the place to pursue the state of our indestructible, fragile Bay, but rather to pay some homage and attention to its remarkable watercraft.

This catalogue of Chesapeake Bay boats does so convincingly well. It is far more than a guidebook to the great variety of watercraft in the Museum's collection and unique to the Bay. It is a living statement at this time that these boats still exist here within the Museum's custody, ashore or afloat. The catalogue describes each boat individually, and a good many of the types exist only in this collection. There are 76 of them.

The Chesapeake Bay watercraft are as unique as the Chesapeake Bay, and that is because of the Bay's unusual singularity. It is unique as a biological nursery and as a microcosm of marine development. It was this way before the European colonization and before the native people came with their log canoes. There is no doubt that the first colonists utilized the native type dugout log craft and used them as a basis for extending their application and development.

There is good reason to believe that the great variety of watercraft whose identity is "Chesapeake-built" results from the resourcefulness of the people who lived on its tidewater shores. They were isolated only by land, but they inherited a world for water transport. The boats they built first and continued to build were products of their own eye and hand. They reflected very little of the European styles nor were they built to any of the rules and dogma that guided European builders. From the colonial period through the first years of the revolution, the term "Chesapeake-built" became a term understood in ports far removed from the Chesapeake. Their distinctive qualities such as rakish appearance and sailing performance particularly made them stand out brightly. They could outsail all others in the early 19th century and many were exported and ultimately copied. This is the heritage of Chesapeake Bay watercraft.

As the 19th century began, the great "sharp-built" Chesapeake schooners appeared in faraway European ports and attracted much envy. Attempts to copy them were mostly unsuccessful because foreign builders were too cautious about their "rules" and feared the lightness of these "foreign" hulls with their great sail spread.

The builders of smaller Chesapeake boats at this time were adapting to local requirements for fishing, oystering, farm produce transport – all of these uses and others in the whole expanse of the Bay from its thousands of tributaries brought out variations in sizes and styles.

Because of the necessity to reach into the upper tributaries, oyster beds and farm wharves, the boats became characteristically rather shoal in draft and of good beam. The centerboard was not invented in the Chesapeake Bay, but it was certainly modified and developed to greater efficiency. Such native types as Chesapeake sloops, bugeyes, pungys, two- and three-sail bateaux, log canoes, and crabbing skiffs, all carry the evidence of this refinement.

On the following pages, the watercraft in the Museum's collection are not categorized by names as in the above examples, but more basically by their hull composition – log-built, round bilge, V- and flat-bottoms. This is a wise decision, to avoid the likely confusion of their names and overlapping types – strange words to the uninitiated. In addition, there are the special-utilization boats, such as gunning boats developed mostly by gunners – waterfowl hunters rather than watermen. There are some in the collection that gained sailing fame and national notice as one-design craft, and for the complete one-of-a-kind there is a final "miscellaneous" chapter.

This catalogue of the Chesapeake Bay Maritime Museum has been long overdue. There are collections of watercraft in other museums, but no others are so extensive either in regional types or in watercraft so closely related to America's maritime development. The boats called "small craft" are as large as the graceful bugeye *Edna E. Lockwood*, 54-1/2 feet by 17 feet, or as small as a push boat for a skipjack. Many of them are built by the hands and skills which descend from the early years of the 19th century. The boatbuilders' names today are much the same. Their work is cut from the same stands of trees as those who sent their boats out of the Chesapeake long ago. These watercraft are truly as unique as the Chesapeake Bay.

Thomas C. Gillmer, Chairman,
Curatorial Committee, 1989-1991

PREFACE

The Chesapeake Bay Maritime Museum has published several booklets on Chesapeake Bay indigenous craft, authored by such noted maritime historians as Howard I. Chapelle and Charles H. Kepner. This catalogue is the first publication to encompass the Museum's entire small craft collection, which is recognized as the largest and most comprehensive collection of Chesapeake Bay watercraft in existence.

The 76 boats in the Museum's collection represent 25 years of acquisition, research and restoration by the Museum's Curatorial and Boat Shop staff and volunteers. The Museum wishes to thank those individuals for their efforts, as well as the many friends and benefactors who donated their boats to enhance the Museum's collection. Without these gifts our precious heritage of small craft would have been lost.

The Chesapeake Bay Maritime Museum also wishes to thank the Maryland Historical Trust for awarding a grant to help fund the cost of publication of the Small Craft Catalogue. We extend a special note of gratitude, also, to our former Curator, Richard J. S. Dodds, for his efforts and enthusiasm in helping to bring this manuscript to fruition. The publication of *A Heritage in Wood* is a landmark in the Museum's efforts to interpret and present Chesapeake Bay history for the public and to preserve it for the future.

John R. Valliant, Director
Chesapeake Bay Maritime Museum

INTRODUCTION

Rosie Parks *under full sail, 1982*

"The Chesapeake Bay has been known from the earliest times for the speed and beauty of its vessels." So wrote Henry Hall in his report on the American shipbuilding industry, compiled for the 10th U.S. Census in 1884. Over a hundred years later, most of the craft that Hall had in mind when writing these words have vanished forever from the waters of the Bay.

The Chesapeake has produced more than its fair share of graceful yet functional craft: Baltimore clippers, pungy schooners, bugeyes, skipjacks, log canoes, crabbing skiffs and a great variety of V-bottom powerboats. A number of pleasure boats, too, have their origin on the Bay such as the Comet Class and Penguin Class sailboats.

The Chesapeake Bay Maritime Museum is fortunate in possessing 76 historic craft in its collection, representing all types of construction methods and spanning a century of boatbuilding tradition. While no original Baltimore clippers or pungy schooners have survived, several bugeyes still exist including *Edna E. Lockwood*, built in 1889, the largest, most important boat in the Museum's collection.

Appropriately, *Lockwood* is a log-built bugeye, direct descendant of the Indian dugouts that predate the settlement at Jamestown, Virginia, in 1607. Dugouts were followed by log canoes, made of two or more logs fastened together, and hollowed out. Indeed, before the advent of the internal combustion engine, the sail-powered log canoe was the boat most used on the Chesapeake. George B. Goode, in *The Fisheries and Fishery Industries of the United States* (1887), reported that more than 6,300 canoes and skiffs were owned in Maryland and Virginia, employing 12,000 watermen in oystering. The dominance of the log canoe partially accounts for the fact that it is the largest class of historic boats to survive today.

The pre-eminent position of the log canoe started to erode with the coming of the 20th century. An increased demand for larger boats with greater displacement and carrying capacity, the disappearance of large trees necessary to provide the logs, and the greater availability of mill-sawn lumber, led to a shift to small frame-built boats, many of them V-bottom.

The rapid growth in the development and availability of cheap and reliable gasoline engines in the early 1900s also contributed to the decline of the log-built boat. At first existing sailing craft were converted to power but the log canoe, with its narrow hull and sharp stern, had a tendency to squat in the water, particularly as engines became larger and more powerful. This problem was accentuated by the fact that the canoe's greatest reserve buoyancy lay in the forward end, where cargo was normally carried. When empty, the weight of the engine aft caused the canoe's stern to sit low in the water.

As a result of the inadequacies of the log canoe hull, more and more boats were built in "deadrise" fashion, as the V-bottom hull is known on the Chesapeake. These were smaller versions of the skipjack or two-sail bateau hull that became popular in the 1890s. These smaller boats were sometimes planked fore and aft on the bottom, but herringbone bottom-planking predominated as it provided greater strength as boats grew larger.

The gasoline engine was welcomed by watermen as a giant step in the conquest of nature and the elimination of human toil. By 1910 *Motorboat* magazine was able to report: "On no body of water in the United States has the development of the motor work boat been brought to so high a standard as on the Chesapeake Bay . . . On this Bay there are fully three thousand motor-propelled craft of various sizes engaged in maritime business in all of its phases. . . ."

The new powerboats varied in appearance depending on where they were built, the differences being most marked in the stern: the diamond or Poquoson stern, round stern, Pot Pie or tuck stern (from the area now known as Wittman, in Talbot County), draketail stern and square or box stern. Most boats built today have the box stern, although now they are generally fiberglass.

Whether power or sail, however, perhaps the most remarkable feature about Chesapeake craft is the fact that so many were built outside of the confines of established boatyards. Henry Hall observed in 1884 that half of the 175 oyster boats produced annually were built by watermen who made their own boats. This backyard boatbuilding tradition is still very much alive today. It does, however, lead to difficulties when trying to track down the history of a particular craft, as few records were kept.

THE SMALL CRAFT COLLECTION

From its very beginning, the Chesapeake Bay Maritime Museum has collected small craft. Its first acquisition was a log canoe built in 1893 (CBMM 63-1-1). Its collection now numbers 76 boats, the most important such collection of Chesapeake craft anywhere. Other good collections exist at Calvert Marine Museum, The Mariners' Museum and the Upper Bay Museum.

What is of interest is how many historic boats have survived into the 1990s. A number of these are actively working, the most significant being Maryland's dwindling fleet of oyster dredging skipjacks, the last remaining work boats to earn their keep by sail alone in North America.

More often than not, a boat is offered to the Museum when it has reached the end of its useful life and is in poor condition. With only limited exhibit and storage space and finite resources to conserve and restore these craft, the Museum has had to turn down a number of deserving boats over the years. But every offer is given careful consideration.

Special consideration must be given to those offers of larger craft that should, or need to, remain in the water. Inevitably this imposes a greater maintenance and upkeep burden with the attendant problem of having to replace original materials from time to time in order to keep the craft serviceable, neat and seaworthy. In the past the Museum, as was common to other maritime museums, tended to over-restore, thereby obliterating or ignoring changes made over time that are significant to the boat's history. Every boat today is now taken on a case-by-case basis with the goal of preserving the physical integrity of the artifact whenever possible. A well-equipped boat shop and marine railway have helped the Museum carry out its responsibility to care for the boats that have been donated.

All boats at the Museum are included in the Museum Small Craft Association's (M.S.C.A) Watercraft Union List, a descriptive list of all watercraft in museums on the North American continent. The Museum's two largest boats, *Edna E. Lockwood* and *Rosie Parks*, are also listed in the National Park Service Inventory of Large Preserved Historic Vessels of the United States and in the World Ship Trust's International Register of Historic Ships. Both *Edna E. Lockwood* and *Kate D.* (*Mustang*) have been nominated to the National Register of Historic Places.

CATALOGUING CONVENTIONS

The small boats of the Chesapeake seem to defy any attempt to place them in a tidy system of classification. However, some order was necessary and most craft have been placed in one of four categories based on type of construction: log-built, V-bottom, round-bilge and flat-bottom. Categorizing boats according to motive power poses a problem as many collection craft were converted from sail to power, and back again in some cases. Classifying boats based on use can be difficult as on the Bay one craft often served a variety of purposes. But this division is well suited to two types of craft: gunning boats and one-design sailboats. So the catalogue is a compromise between two systems – construction and use. This avoids a certain artificiality that comes with trying to fit such a diverse collection into one classification type.

Each entry gives the date and place of build and builder, if known. Dimensions are overall length and beam. At the bottom of every entry is the donor's name and Museum accession number (a unique number given to each object in the collection). Specific bibliographic references to a particular boat or builder are given with the entry. For further reading a general bibliography is given in the back. The description of each boat is based on the best available information in Museum files. We would welcome any additions or corrections to what is recorded.

The drawings that are reproduced in this catalogue are from the Museum's boat plans collection.

ACKNOWLEDGMENTS

Planning for this Small Craft Catalogue started in the summer of 1984 when the Museum began a regular program of taking the lines off the most important boats in the collection. Up to that time, drawings were only available for the two largest craft – *Edna E. Lockwood* and *Rosie Parks*. In that year six boats were "documented" by recording the lines, construction details and offsets – sufficient information to construct duplicates, if necessary.

The process of producing these drawings was kept simple and traditional. "Taking off the lines" generally consists of establishing reference lines and planes and making measurements from reference lines to the hull within the planes. Measurements were made in English units and are accurate to an eighth of an inch.

The Museum was fortunate in having two talented young people who helped to document our small craft on paper – Susan Kaighn and Scott Black. Their work, which was funded by the Ernest Tucker Memorial Boatbuilding Apprenticeship Endowment, established by Jane Foster Tucker, appears in this catalogue. Susan was assisted by John G. Lord, retired naval architect, who, until he moved out of the area, gave very generously of his time and expertise. John devised a pantograph that could draw to scale both the inside and outside of a boat's side, at each station, to determine hull thickness. This was a particular problem with log canoes, whose sides vary in thickness.

Volunteers Leavenworth Holden and Josef Liener have also documented boats at the Museum, and their drawings may be seen in this publication. Their invaluable assistance has also extended beyond the Museum, to take the lines off endangered historic craft that are owned by private individuals. Joe has been the Museum's Small Craft Consultant for many years and his advice and guidance have always been generously given and much appreciated.

Copies of the drawings made by interns and volunteers have been made available to the public to satisfy a growing interest in historic Chesapeake Bay craft. However, it was long felt that the Museum should go one step further and combine many of the drawings with photographs and histories into a catalogue of the small craft collection. The impetus for this publication was provided by Thomas C. Gillmer, who, as Chairman of the Curatorial Committee, gave the project a high priority.

Work started in earnest in the summer of 1990 when two interns, Pete Lesher and Christopher Semancik, were employed to review all the records pertaining to the collection, to seek more information from donors and other sources where necessary, and to draft the introductory sections and individual entries. The finished product incorporates much of their excellent work. Elaine Jones, Curatorial Secretary, had the unenviable job of entering much of the data into the computer and making the many revisions and updates. Norman Plummer and Leslie Grunden did a major job of proofreading and editing.

Lastly, the following individuals kindly agreed to review the manuscript and offered many valuable suggestions and comments: Robert H. Burgess, John G. Earle, Thomas C. Gillmer, Joseph Gregory, Jim Holt, Leavenworth Holden, Tom Howell, Josef Liener and Richard Scofield. Any errors of fact or omissions are solely the fault of the Editors, however.

LOG-BUILT BOATS

Possibly the type of boat most closely associated with the Chesapeake Bay is the log canoe. A truly native American craft, it was the workhorse of the Chesapeake, akin to the horse and buggy on land, and has survived from the colonial period to the present day. William A. Davis, writing in the *The Rudder* magazine in April 1909, described the craft as the "best hardweather and general utility boats in the world."

The first European settlers on the Chesapeake found the native Americans using dugout canoes of loblolly pine and tulip poplar. They were hollowed out with fire, and oyster shells were used to scrape away the charred wood. Lack of skilled boatbuilders forced settlers to adapt the Indian canoes to their own needs. The use of steel tools enabled them to sharpen the ends of the log and, later, to join two logs together to make a larger boat. Canoes were at first paddled or poled but later rigged for sail.

The most famous of Chesapeake dugouts was undoubtedly the *Methodist*, fashioned from an enormous tree to produce a boat between 20 and 30 feet long by five feet wide. She was built in the early 1800s for use by Joshua Thomas, the "Parson of the Islands", on his circuit of the Bay's inhabited islands.

With the expansion of the seafood industry following the Civil War, increasing numbers of canoes were built (old timers usually pronounced them "cunoes", while their owners were known as "cunners"). The few simple tools required, and the lack of mill-sawn lumber in the small waterfront communities, contributed to the canoe's pre-eminent position.

By the latter part of the 19th century, with the depletion of the largest trees and the demand for larger craft, canoes were being made of three and, later, five logs fastened together. Centerboards were not fitted to the smaller canoes until the late 19th century; a shallow keel sufficed for the purpose.

John B. Harrison (1865-1945) as a young man.

Canoes were not "laid down" in the manner of plank-on-frame boats and were seldom built in shipyards. Length and width were the only specifications required. A builder would select his trees and cut them in late winter when the sap was low. After a tree was felled, it would be shaped into a "chunk" where it lay (log built boats are still called "chunk boats" in the Lower Bay). The chunks were brought to the building site, further shaped, then fastened together with wrought iron drift pins. They were then hollowed out with an adze, plane and slick. Straight trees were chosen for the keel log and garboard logs and naturally curved ones for the wing logs. Wooden trunnels and iron drift pins held the logs together. The sides were built up with planks or "risers," with construction varying from region to region. Further details of the log construction process may be found in Marion Brewington's *Chesapeake Bay Log Canoes and Bugeyes*.

Although there were many varieties of canoes, Brewington identified three broad categories, generally divided by region: Poquoson, Pocomoke and Tilghman. Those of Virginia origin and construction are called Poquoson canoes. The entire hull is log-built, up to the sheer or "bends." When rigged with a jib, a stub bowsprit extended forward without a longhead. A single mast was carried.

The Pocomoke, Nanticoke, or "rising strake" canoe had its origins on the Lower Eastern Shore of Maryland. The least common of the three types, it is distinguished by planks fastened in lapstrake fashion to the outside of the wing logs. These planks then have the appearance of "bends" or wales as typified by the heavy sheer planking on framed vessels. The rising strakes are fastened on after the tops of the wing logs have been trimmed and any necessary additional chunks scarfed to the ends. The washboards, centerboard, and other interior fittings are not unlike the Poquoson canoes, except for the mast step, fashioned from a large natural crook to fit in the bottom of the canoe and extended up the sides as a pair of frames.

Tilghman canoes are the most refined design, with the rising planks fitted in carvel fashion and fastened to the top of the wing logs. As with the other types of canoes, the raked stem and stern-posts are straight, but in Tilghman canoes, the bow is extended with a graceful longhead and head rails under the bowsprit. This was often adorned with carved and painted trailboards and a billethead, or occasionally a small figurehead. Tilghman canoes were generally finer at bow and stern than those of the Lower Bay. The more open waters and stronger winds of the Lower Bay demanded a fuller hull that had greater buoyancy.

In a 1933 interview, boatbuilder John B. Harrison credited William N. Covington of Tilghman Island with introducing the centerboard to canoes in the 1870s. Other sources, however, credit log canoe builder Robert D. Lambdin, of St. Michaels.

The canoe rig also saw its greatest refinement in the Tilghman region, on Maryland's Eastern Shore. In two-masted canoes, although the forward mast is the larger, the masts are designated, in schooner fashion, as "fore" and "main." While both Pocomoke and Tilghman canoes are rigged with two masts, the Pocomoke canoes stepped a small "jigger" (or "spanker") sail forward of the foremast. The spar for the jigger shares a step with the foremast and rakes forward. In Tilghman canoes, a jib is raised on the forestay. The fore and mainsail are jib-headed and they carry a sprit ("spreet") rather than a boom. A club bent onto the squared-off clew of the sail fits on the end of the "spreet."

This full rig was only occasionally used on the working canoes, but was developed further when the canoes were raced. Racing was a natural outgrowth of the keen rivalry that existed between log canoe owners and their desire to be first to the buyer with oysters. The earliest recorded organized log canoe race took place off St. Michaels in 1859, and later races were held at Cambridge, Oxford and Solomons Island. As racing grew in popularity in the late 19th century, canoes built especially for racing appeared. The masts were heightened and the foot of the jib extended to increase sail area. The club at the clew of the fore and main was lengthened to make the sails more distinctly quadrilateral. A "swinging" or "balanced" jib with its foot bent on a jibboom that extended beyond the end of the bowsprit

was introduced. Additional experimental sails appeared in the 20th century, including a kite (a triangular topsail), square sails hoisted aloft for downwind sailing, and staysails. To keep these severely over-canvassed racers from turning over, hikingboards, 12 to 15 feet long by about 10 inches wide, were tucked under the leeward washboard and allowed to extend far off the windward washboard. The crews scramble in and out on these boards and act as movable ballast.

The ubiquitous working log canoe could be found in every creek and river on the Bay. They were relatively inexpensive to build, held up well, and were ideally suited for oystering. Canoes possessed good carrying capacity, no frames to interfere with shoveling oysters, wide gunwales for the tongers, and a sprit rig that enabled the mainsail to be furled to the mast, out of the way.

Average length of oyster tonging canoes was 25 to 30 feet, which suited the short, choppy seas found in the Bay. Rather than riding up and down each wave crest, their length was supported by several crests at a time. Oysters were plucked from the shallow beds by watermen using long-handled wooden tongs.

However, in the early 1800s, as northern oyster beds were nearly exhausted, New England schooners appeared on the Bay to harvest oysters with heavy dredges. This practice was outlawed by Virginia and subsequently by Maryland in 1820 so as not to drive the native oystermen out of business. The Maryland legislature legalized the "scrape," a small, hand-operated oyster dredge, for use in Somerset County waters beginning in 1854, and log canoes increased in size to provide the necessary pulling power for the scrape. This device was legalized for Dorchester County in 1870 and for Talbot County in 1874, spreading the larger log canoes to new regions. Out of these larger canoes evolved the brogan, built with partial decks instead of washboards and with interiors divided into covered holds. A small cabin forward provided accommodation for the crew and allowed the boats to venture out overnight and farther from their home waters. The two-masted brogan averaged 40-45 feet in length and was made from five to seven logs.

In 1865 Maryland amended its oyster conservation laws to allow dredging (or "drudging" as it was more commonly called) under sail in specified areas by licensed Maryland vessels. To take advantage of the new opportunity, even larger canoes were built, of seven or nine logs, and fully decked. The result was a new type of craft — the "buckeye," or "bugeye" as it was later known. It carried a triangular fore, main, and jib with

Lockwood **towards the end of her career, sailing with reefed fore and mainsail, Captain Ivy McNamara at the wheel.**

multiple reef points to maintain the most desirable speed for dredging.

No one knows for sure where the term bugeye originated. It may be from the Scotch word "buckie" meaning oyster shell or the fact that the hawse holes, when seen from ahead, seem to resemble bug's eyes – hence the name.

The earliest bugeyes had external keels to provide lateral resistance, as did the early canoes, but the centerboard proved to be a better solution, given the shoal waters common in the Chesapeake.

The log-bottom bugeyes were later supplemented with frame-built versions, both of which, along with the oyster sloop and schooner, were ultimately replaced in the dredging fleet by the skipjack, a less expensive "box-built" boat.

Henry Hall, in his 1884 report on shipbuilding in America, observed that log bugeyes cost $600 to $800 to build and could carry 200 to 300 bushels. Framed boats cost $1,000 to $ 2,500 depending on size. Plank on frame construction allowed builders to construct round-stern bugeyes, in an effort to overcome the small working area inherent on the sharp-sterned log bugeyes.

Bugeyes such as the Museum's *Edna E. Lockwood* were the ultimate development of the log-built hull. With the disappearance of large trees suitable for building and the rapid acceptance of the V-bottom boat, few canoes were built after 1920.

Interestingly, even with the coming of the internal combustion engine in the early 20th century, a number of canoes were built along traditional sailing lines but intended for mechanical power at the outset. One such transitional boat is the *Alverta*, built in 1908.

What is remarkable is the Chesapeake canoe's longevity and adaptability. A fleet of racing canoes, many built in the 19th century, still competes in the annual races held on Maryland's Eastern Shore. And one of the last log-hulled boats to work on the Bay, *F. D. Crockett*, built in 1924, still works as a crab dredger out of Hampton, Virginia, immaculately maintained, and a uniquely Chesapeake boat.

Single-Log Dugout

Date and place of build unknown
15' 4" x 1' 6"

Only a fragment of this canoe remains and its origin is obscure. The hull was carved out of a log, then filled with water and the water heated with hot rocks. The softened sides were then bent outward and stretcher pieces were inserted to hold the shape of the spread sides. This allowed the builder to make a canoe of greater beam with a small log. Cleat marks on the inside of the canoe mark the positions of these spreader pieces, now missing.

This "boiled log dugout" is of foreign origin, made from a wood not found in the United States, and probably came to the Chesapeake as deck cargo on a freighter. The craft was found floating on the Gunpowder River after a flood. Only a 'midship section of the hull survives, comprising perhaps half of the original length.

Donor: Charles E. Hopwood

68-84-1

Single-Log Dugout

Built circa 1920, Goshen Farm, Gloucester, Virginia, by Robert Booth
16' 4" x 1' 11"

This log dugout canoe was built by a full-blooded American Indian, Robert Booth, who was a former slave at Goshen Farm in Gloucester, Virginia. Mr. Booth built this canoe on the Goshen Farm when he was in his eighties. He used the canoe for fishing the Ware River, which ran by Goshen Farm. When he died in 1923 at the age of 88, he left the canoe in the marshes of Warehouse Cove, on the Ware River.

This craft was perhaps one of the last dugouts built on the Chesapeake and is a direct link with the Indian canoes of the colonial period.

Donors: Mr. and Mrs. Fred Lyman

65-127-1

Dugout built by Robert Booth.

W. A. Johns
Three-Log Canoe

Date of build unknown, Poquoson, Virginia
34' 9" x 7' 6"

This log canoe appears to be of three-log construction, but there are small filler pieces running the length of the hull between the center and garboard logs, probably due to later repairs. She is built in the Poquoson style, of loblolly pine.

Her early history is unknown, although Rufus Ruark of Deltaville purchased the canoe around 1933 from neighbor Dr. William P. Gwathney. Ruark, who died in 1967, used the craft for oyster patent tonging, and she was equipped with a two-cylinder Palmer engine. During this time she was an open boat with a small, removable cuddy located forward.

A cabin, two masts and a seven-horsepower engine were added by owner William Allen Johns, Jr. when he rebuilt her for pleasure sailing in the early 1970s. Engine and cabin were later removed by the Museum when she was restored to sailing status. She has not been sailed since the early 1980s.

Donors: Dr. and Mrs. William A. Johns
in memory of W. A. Johns, Jr.

73-27-1

W. A. Johns *as restored by W. A. Johns, Jr. with cruising cabin and ketch rig.*

Marianne
Three-Log Tilghman Canoe

Built prior to 1916,
Queen Anne's County, Maryland
Attributed to John Reese of Bryantown
22' x 4' 10"

Marianne *racing on the Miles River.*

Little is known of the early history of this craft, but in January 1956, when Joseph A. Miller of Queenstown purchased *Marianne* from Edward Severa, she was a sloop-rigged pleasure boat. Mr. Severa had converted the boat back to sail after she had been used for crabbing with an engine. For several years he kept her at Crab Alley Creek. When Dr. E. C. H. Schmidt bought the canoe in 1960, he had her altered for racing. A two-masted Tilghman racing rig was added, with sitka spruce spars and dacron sails. He added a bumpkin, lengthened the bowsprit, and added scrollwork at the bow.

Marianne was raced for a number of years, but her small size put her at a disadvantage. After she was donated to the Museum in 1968 she continued to race, but was eventually retired.

Marianne remains in good condition, complete with her racing rig. She is a good example of the conversion of a working canoe to a racing canoe.

Donor: Dr. E. C. H. Schmidt
68-124-1

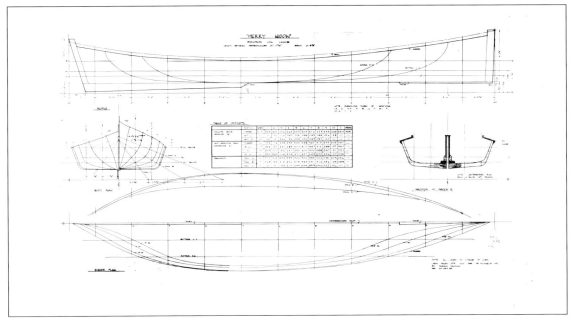

Merry Widow
Three-Log Poquoson Canoe

Built 1910, St. Mary's County, Maryland
Attributed to Captain Will Knotts
29' 0-3/8" x 6' 9-3/4"

Merry Widow is a typical example of a Poquoson log canoe, with straight stem and sternpost, cambered decks, and washboards, rigged with a single mast and spritsail. She has no rudder, but would have been steered with an oar.

Merry Widow was acquired by a group of Jesuit priests at St. Inigoes Church on Priest's Point, St. Mary's County, in the late 1920s or early 1930s.

By that time she had been motorized with a five horsepower Palmer engine. The priests changed her name to Little Flower and used her for trips on St. Inigoes Creek and St. Mary's River.

Will Knotts was a local boatbuilder, active in the early 20th century, who built several canoes, mainly of two or three logs. Knotts had a reputation as an excellent craftsman. How the canoe came to the Eastern Shore is unknown.

Merry Widow has been restored for exhibit, but is no longer in floating condition.

Donor: Curtis Applegarth

67-129-1

Merry Widow *shortly after arrival at CBMM, 1968.*

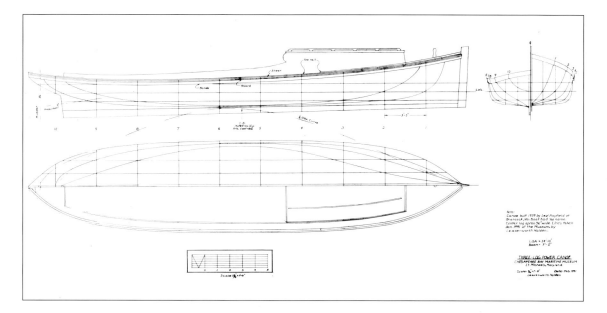

Three-Log Power Canoe

Built 1939, Onancock, Virginia, by Levi Rayfield
34' 10" x 7' 0"

This log canoe, remarkable for its relatively late date of build, was made expressly for power and shows a hull shape adapted to this purpose. Levi Rayfield carved it when he was 40, and used it for racing and pleasure. It was the only canoe he ever built.

The logs were purchased from Frank Riley of Cashville, Virginia. The keel log is extremely large, possibly the largest of any canoe in the collection.

Built fairly straight and narrow, she never had a centerboard or sailing rig and her first engine was a Model A Ford conversion. She was painted in traditional workboat colors: white topsides and red below the waterline. A large cabin was fitted forward.

William Earl Howard of Leemont, Virginia, bought the boat around 1971 and soon after rebuilt the canoe almost down to the chunks. Much of the new work was mahogany, including the cabin. He added more sheer, building up the bow and stern, and cut a decorative bead along the rail. The new engine box was of cedar, as were the squat boards, which could be adjusted with bottle screws. In place of the old wooden rudder, he installed a new one of stainless steel, steered by a stainless steel T tiller. The chain sprocket was replaced with cable steering. A brass steering wheel was mounted behind the cabin.

Howard installed a Lincoln Continental V-8 in

Levi Rayfield's log canoe under construction, 1939.

the canoe, making the boat very fast. When he sold the boat to Mr. and Mrs. David Bundick of Modest Town, Virginia, in 1981, he removed the engine, as the Bundicks intended to convert the boat to sail. This conversion never took place and the Museum acquired the boat in 1986.

Purchase

88-25-1

Fly
Five-Log Poquoson Canoe
Date and place of build unknown
22' 6" x 5' 3"

Though the origin of this canoe is unknown, the boat was repaired in 1930 by Captain Edward Leatherbury of Shadyside, Maryland. Leatherbury named the canoe *Fly*; he preferred three letter names because they were easier to carve on the trailboards. The strip-planked deck may have been put on at this time, as the workmanship is good and Leatherbury is known to have built strip-plank decks on boats of his own construction, such as the deadrise sailing skiff *Ava* (CBMM 78-34-1). Although built as a five-log canoe, the garboard logs were altered and partially replaced with graving pieces, giving the appearance of a three-log canoe.

Fly retains her rudder, centerboard, and removable floorboards, but her rig is missing. She would have been sloop-rigged, with a small jib on a stub bowsprit.

Wells E. Hunt donated *Fly* to Mystic Seaport Museum in 1951, and for many years she represented the Chesapeake Bay log canoe in its collection.

Donor: Mystic Seaport Museum

85-2-1

Five-log Poquoson canoe Fly on exhibit at CBMM, 1992.

Kate D.
Five-Log Canoe

Built 1904-1907, near Saxis, Virginia,
by Edward Barney Moore
46' 7-1/2" x 11' 4"   Official No. 219054

This five-log canoe was built by E. Barney Moore, assisted by his son, E. Jeeter Moore. She was built by "rack of eye," or without plans, which accounts for her starboard side having 4 inches more beam than the port side. Her five loblolly pine logs were all taken from the same marsh, the keel log measuring 34 inches wide by 6 inches thick.

Moore moved to Saxis in the late 19th century from Poquoson, Virginia, where he learned his trade. Although official records indicate Saxis as place of build, it is possible that *Kate D.* was built in nearby Sanford where trees were more plentiful.

Kate D. was not licensed until 1919. At the time she was owned by John R. Drewer of Saxis, who named the boat after his wife Kate Elizabeth Drewer. It was at this period that she was "raised-on," or rebuilt as a powerboat. Family history and recollections of old-time residents state that *Kate D.* started as a two masted sailing brogan.

Until sold out of the Drewer family in 1938, *Kate D.* was used for freighting and, as a powerboat, was fitted with a small pilothouse aft and a 24-horsepower Clay engine, with a gaff-headed steadying sail set forward. For many years she was Saxis' main link with the larger town of Crisfield.

From 1959 until 1987 the canoe was owned by Gerald T. Morton who changed her name to *Mustang* and used her for chartering out of Annapolis. During this time she carried a two

Kate D. was named after Kate Drewer.

masted rig and large main cabin. In 1980 she was nominated to the National Register of Historic Places. *Kate D.* has always been described as a brogan and has the dimensions of a typical brogan, although to date no photographic evidence has come to light showing her appearance before 1919.

As a brogan, she would be, like the bugeye *Edna E. Lockwood*, another rare log-built survivor. The only other known brogan is the hull of the 40-foot *Shamrock*, at Calvert Marine Museum, built circa 1908. Condition of *Kate D.*'s hull is poor and she remains in an unrestored state.

Donor: Paul G. Dix

89-34-1

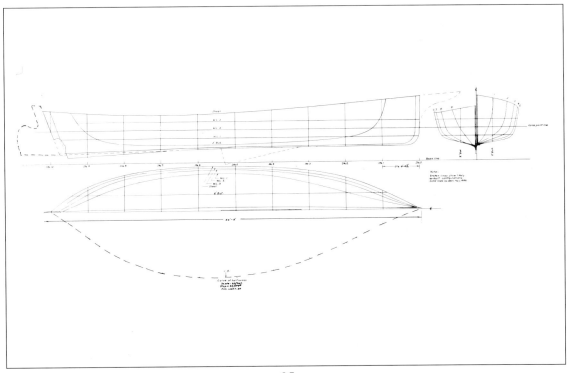

Five-Log Tilghman Canoe

Built 1893, St. Michaels, Maryland,
by Robert Dawson Lambdin
31' 2-1/2" x 6' 7-1/2"

This unnamed canoe was built by the well-known St. Michaels boatbuilder Robert Lambdin (1849-1938). Lambdin built many prominent Bay craft, including the first round-stern bugeye, *Cynthia*. He also built the canoes *Chesapeake*, which appeared at the Chicago World's Fair in 1893, and *Dashaway*, which never lost a race and lasted 52 years.

Lambdin's account book shows this canoe was built for C. Howard Lloyd of Wye Island. The

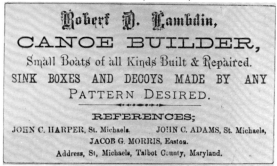

contract called for "a canoe 30 ft. long and 6-1/2 ft. wide and furnish spars and spreets and rowlocks for $160.00." The resultant craft was finished in two months, the final cost being $212.97.

The canoe is of unusually superior construction. Lambdin rabbeted the logs together using a V-joint at each end, a detail not found in canoes by other builders. The canoe is built in the Tilghman style, with the feather edges of the garboard and wing logs cut off, and with drift-bolted filler pieces extending from these logs to the stem and sternpost. The sheer is fastened in a similar fashion. The logs are fastened with both iron drift pins and brass butterfly fastenings. The hull has little deadrise amidships, and the bilge turns sharply along the wing logs.

Howard Lloyd, her first owner, gave the canoe to Gustif F. Meilke of Tunis Mills, who had farmed Wye House Farm and the adjoining Grange Farm for many years. In 1952, she was acquired by Mr. and Mrs. Edgington Franklin, who donated the canoe to the Museum.

At some point the sailing rig of this canoe was removed, and an engine installed. At this time, the centerboard trunk was cut out and the centerboard slot filled. A strongback was installed across the logs approximately one-third of the distance from the bow, crossing the former

centerboard slot. This prevented engine vibrations from separating the logs. Forward of this strongback and at the end of the wing logs is a pair of heavy frames extending from the top of the garboard logs to the sheer, bracing the filler pieces and the sheer strake. The center log was bored for a shaft, and there is evidence of a stuffing box. The sternpost is partially cut away to allow for the propeller.

Today, only the hull remains, the deck and washboards having been removed. The logs have split apart and show dry rot in places, but these defects reveal the construction details and masterful workmanship in this canoe. This craft has the distinction of being the first boat donated to the Museum.

Donor: Mrs. Edgington Franklin

63-1-1

Five-log canoe built by Robert D. Lambdin, on exhibit in 1990. Visible are the rabbeted logs and filled centerboard slot.

Robert D. Lambdin with one of his log canoe models, at the Old Men's Home, Baltimore.

Miller, Ben H. "A Veteran Log Canoe Builder." *Sun* (Baltimore) 9 Jun. 1935.

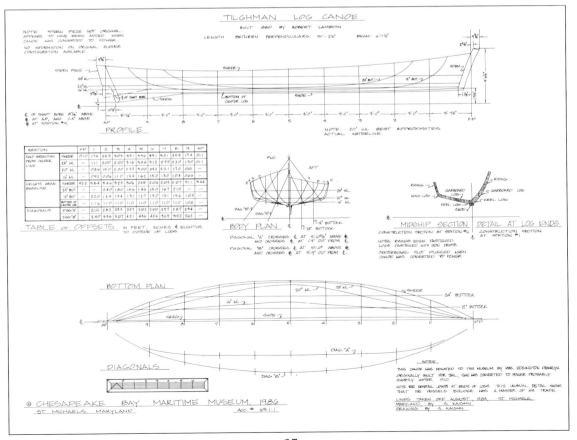

Lillian R. as a powerboat in 1962.

Lillian R.
Five-Log Pocomoke Canoe

Built circa 1903–1905, Elliott Island, Maryland,
by Sam or Herman Jones
34' 3" x 7' 0-1/4"

This canoe was built in the Pocomoke or Nanticoke style, typical of Maryland's Lower Eastern Shore. The bottom is shaped out of five loblolly pine logs, and the topsides are of a single "rising strake." This plank is fastened to the logs in a lapstrake fashion, and the cambered washboards are braced with white oak frames.

Willard Johnson of Dorchester County owned, sailed, and reportedly raced *Lillian R.* After World War II the canoe was converted to power, and under the ownership of Armond Hayward of Golden Hill, Maryland, she worked in the oyster tonging fleet in the Fishing Bay area until 1962. She was then laid up until purchased by Harry C. Thompson of Easton and donated to the Museum.

Lillian R. is no longer in floating condition and shows considerable dry rot in her logs, planks and frames. This is one of the few surviving examples of a rising strake canoe. Canoes of this type frequently carried a jigger or "stick-up" sail forward of the foremast. This small, triangular sail was laced to a spar stepped in the eyes of the boat, occasionally sharing a step with the foremast and raking forward at almost 45 degrees.

Donor: Harry C. Thompson

69-41-1

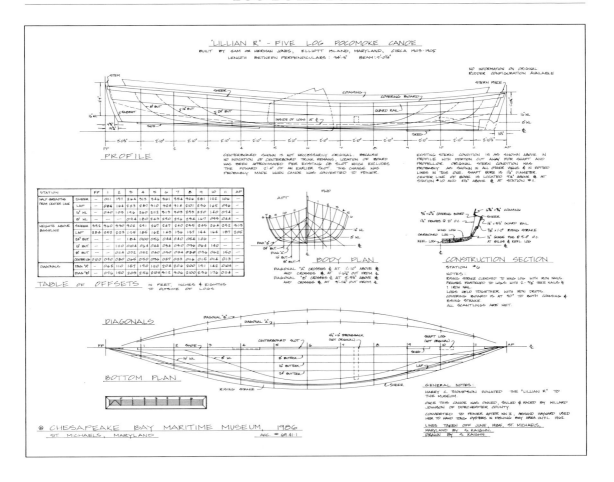

"LILLIAN R" - FIVE LOG POCOMOKE CANOE

BUILT BY SAM OR HERMAN JONES, ELLIOTT ISLAND, MARYLAND, CIRCA 1903-1905
LENGTH BETWEEN PERPENDICULARS : 34'-5"   BEAM: 7'-0½"

PROFILE

BODY PLAN

CONSTRUCTION SECTION

TABLE OF OFFSETS   IN FEET, INCHES & EIGHTHS
TO OUTSIDE OF LOGS

DIAGONALS

BOTTOM PLAN

© CHESAPEAKE BAY MARITIME MUSEUM, 1986
ST. MICHAELS, MARYLAND   ACC #69.41.1

Alverta
Five-Log Canoe

Built 1908, Kent Island, Maryland,
by Walter Gardiner and Joseph Thompson
32' 2" x 6' 6"

Joseph A. Thompson, builder of Alverta, *and his wife, Etta, circa 1890.*

A*lverta* is an important example of the early development of motorized workboats on the Chesapeake. She was built of logs, in canoe fashion, specifically for power. She never had a centerboard or sailing rig. Nevertheless, the hull form is relatively unchanged from that of the sailing canoes. The familiar deadrise power workboat was yet to appear.

The hull was begun by Walter Gardiner, who injured his knee with an adze and was unable to finish it. Work was continued by Joseph A. Thompson, (1864-1937) brother of Eugene Thompson, builder of the racing log canoe *Silver Heel*. The Thompson family of Kent Island has produced a number of fine boatbuilders and still operates a boatshop in Dominion.

Alverta's previous owners include Leroy Smith, John A. Gardiner and Phil King. Mr. King's wife was Alverta, and the boat was named for her. Other owners include Delbert Baker and his

Alverta in Cambridge harbor before donation to CBMM.

brother-in-law, Douglas Ferris.

Though originally powered with a one-cylinder engine typical of the period in which she was built, when she came to the Museum *Alverta* had a 1951 Jeep four-cylinder engine made by Kaiser. This engine was equipped with a car transmission and was cooled with a car radiator.

Alverta has a small cuddy cabin forward and is steered with a typical Chesapeake steering stick, attached to the starboard coaming and connected to the tiller by means of rope. At some time the cabin was altered when a replacement engine was fitted.

Donors: Douglas and Joyce Ferris

81-29-1

Taking the lines off Old Point, *CBMM, August 1985.*

Old Point
Seven-Log Crab Dredger

Built 1909, Poquoson, Virginia, by J. G. Wornom
51' 9" x 12' 10"   Official No. 206439

O*ld Point* represents yet another variation on the log-built hull. Crab dredging is permitted in Virginia from December through March utilizing two large dredges resembling oyster dredges with longer tines. Heavy metal rollers protect the rails from wear. The dredges are secured to a heavy post in the center of the vessel and raised with mechanical winders located below decks on either side of the post. These "deck boats", as they are known in Virginia, were also used for freighting in the off-season.

Old Point had two hatches over the hold in the middle of the vessel, a small one just forward of the pilothouse and a large hatch just abaft the mast. The pilothouse had two bunks (the upper one remains), and there was a swing down bunk in the engine room. The fuel tank was located above deck behind the pilothouse. Forward of the mast was a forepeak with a raised companionway, with a barrel for fresh water forward of this structure. A steadying sail was formerly used with the gaff doubling as a cargo hoist.

J. G. Wornom built *Old Point* for J. I. and George C. Wainwright, but for much of her life (1913-1956) *Old Point* was owned by the Bradshaw family of Hampton, Virginia. During these years the Bradshaws used *Old Point* as a crab dredger in the winter, to freight fish in the summer, and to carry oysters from the James River during the fall, selling their catch to the Ballard Fish and Oyster Co. in Norfolk, Virginia.

In 1956, *Old Point* was sold to the Old Dominion Crab Company, which used her for crab dredging. At some time after 1956, *Old Point* suffered a fire in the bow that destroyed the forepeak. Some charred frames are still visible; the damaged portion of her logs was filled with Portland cement. It may have been at this time that the

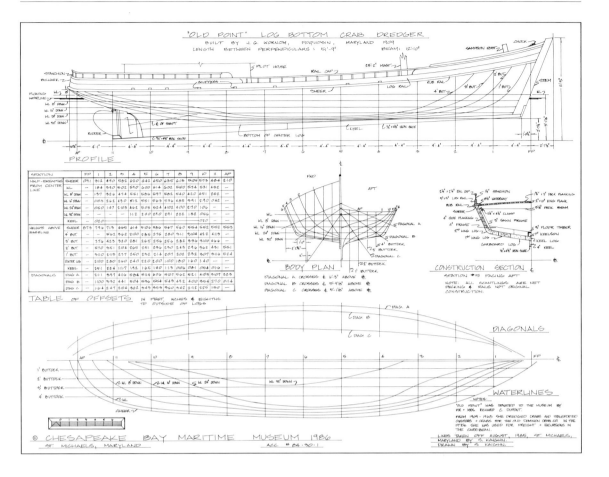

galley and bunks were added above the engine room. In 1968, she was sold to Norman F. Williams, who changed her name to *Miss Terry*. She passed through several other ownerships, being used for freight and excursions in the Caribbean until she was donated to the Museum in 1984.

The Museum intends to restore *Old Point* closer to her earlier working appearance by replacing the existing single hatch between mast and pilothouse, refitting the forepeak, and installing a large mast and boom with steadying sail. She is considered to be the last-but-one, log-hull deck boat to work on the Chesapeake. The 1924 *F. D. Crockett* is still, remarkably, making a living on the Bay.

Donors: Mr. and Mrs. Richard C. duPont

84-30-1

Edna E. Lockwood
Nine-Log Bugeye

Built 1889, Tilghman Island, Maryland,
by John B. Harrison
54' 8" x 17' 2"   Official No. 136088

In 1889, at the age of 24, John B. Harrison of Tilghman Island built *Edna E. Lockwood*, the seventh of 18 bugeyes he was to build. Harrison also built the well known log canoes *Jay Dee* and *Flying Cloud*.

Edna E. Lockwood was probably built on Chicken Point at the southeast end of Knapps Narrows. Her hull is hewn of nine pine logs, and is several inches wider on her starboard side. This asymmetry in her hull allows her to sail closer to the wind on port tack, to dredge better on port tack, and to come about to starboard more easily. She was built with a sharp stern, but a platform known as a patent stern was added sometime around 1910 to provide more working space aft for handling the pushboat. With her centerboard up, *Edna E. Lockwood* draws only 2.7 feet, and her registered capacity is 9.83 tons net.

Built for Daniel W. Haddaway of Tilghman Island, a neighbor to John B. Harrison, *Edna E. Lockwood* dredged for oysters through the winter and carried freight, such as lumber, grain or produce, after the dredging season ended.

She worked faithfully for various owners, mainly out of Cambridge, Maryland, until she stopped "drudging" in 1967. In 1973 she was donated to the Museum.

Edna E. Lockwood was dismantled down to her nine logs in 1975 and rebuilt over the next several years. In this process, she was built stronger than the original, with the addition of 21 natural knees of hackmatack, new frames that extended all the way to her keel log instead of the wing log, a heavier kingplank, and more tie rods. Her oyster dredging gear, removed during the refit, has not been replaced. Today, she is again in sailing condition and is raced on occasion by the Museum against other large Chesapeake workboats. *Lockwood* is a rare survivor, the last of the log-hull bugeyes afloat, and is without doubt the most significant boat in the Small Craft Collection. She was nominated to the National Register of Historic Places in 1986.

Despite extensive research, the origin of the name *Edna E. Lockwood* still remains obscure.

Donor: John R. Kimberly

67-155-1

Lockwood *sailing home from Annapolis in her 100th year, 1989.*

Kepner, Charles H. *The Edna E. Lockwood.* St. Michaels, Md. Chesapeake Bay Maritime Museum, 1979.

Line, Lila. "Wooden Ships, Iron Men." *Star Democrat* (Easton) 3 Dec. 1976.

Paddock, Eric. "Life of John B. Harrison is a History of Boat Building on the Bay." *Talbot Banner* (Easton) 10 Oct. 1975.

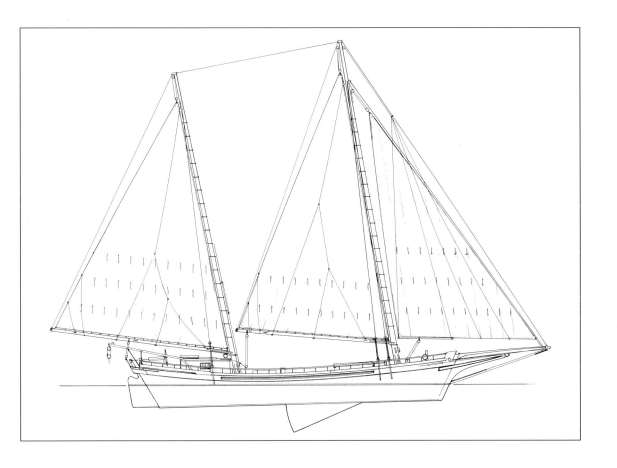

ROUND-BILGE BOATS

The first sailing craft built in North America were fashioned after those European models with which colonists were familiar – round-bilge and plank-on-frame construction. They were made to satisfy an immediate need for boats for fishing, transportation and exploring. Although the lack of skilled craftsmen was an obstacle, both Virginia and Maryland had well-developed shipbuilding industries by 1700. The bulk of the colonial vessels were small sloops, and craft described as shallops and pinnaces.

With the development of two-masted schooners in America in the late 1700s, Chesapeake builders began to specialize in a particularly fast and handsome type known as Baltimore clippers. By the early 1800s larger craft, such as brigs, were also being built. This tradition of building round-bilge sloops and schooners carried into the late 19th century, but would disappear with the coming of the engine and the V-bottom boat.

With the popularity of the log canoe as the small workboat of choice among Chesapeake watermen, the round-bilge boat never took hold as it did for the larger sailing craft. Log canoes were easier to build and cheaper than their plank-on-frame counterparts, and would often hold up better under the harsh conditions found in the oyster industry. The absence of frames in a log canoe made it easier to shovel oysters from the bottom of the boat.

Plank-on-frame boats that were employed in the fisheries could be most often found in the far north of the Bay and were either migrants from the Delaware River area or were built in specialized boatshops in the Upper Bay, often

The graceful lines of the Yankee skiff are evident in this view, taken in the CBMM Small Boat Shed.

showing a New Jersey influence.

Another small craft commonly built in the round-bilge fashion was the yawl boat carried by larger Bay sailing craft – schooners and sloops hauling freight and dredging oysters. The long, narrow and heavy log canoe did not lend itself to being a ship's boat that had to be rowed and carried in davits when not in use. In the 20th century, however, the round-bilge yawl boat was replaced by the V-bottom version. Also, some yawl boats which were originally sculled or rowed became engine-powered "pushboats".

Not surprisingly, most of the boats in this chapter show characteristics atypical of the Chesapeake, none more so than the "Yankee skiff." The graceful, lapstrake Yankee skiff is also known as the Staten Island Skiff or Raritan Bay Oyster skiff, after the area in New York where it originated. Henry Hall, in his 1884 report on the American shipbuilding industry, reported seeing 125 of these oyster skiffs off Perth Amboy and its vicinity. In 1906, *Forest and Stream* published a description and set of lines for a typical Yankee skiff.

Eventually these craft found their way to the Chesapeake. A number of New York and New England oyster packers moved down to the Chesapeake Bay in the boom years of the region's oyster industry, including Peter Van Name, who settled on the York River in Virginia in the 1870s and popularized these skiffs. Some packing houses in Virginia brought these skiffs from the north and rented them to oyster tongers. Today only a few of these migrants have survived, all in museums.

Whether either of the two round-bilge shad skiffs in the Museum's collection originated north of the Bay, like the Yankee skiff, is not known. Several boat shops in the Upper Bay were building these craft, which are similar to the Delaware River gillnet skiffs.

During the heyday of the Bay's great shad fishery, shad and herring were caught in the spring as they made their way to their breeding grounds in the Susquehanna River. Typically three men would man a shad skiff; two to haul in the net over the stern and the third at the oars in the bow to help hold the skiff into the tide and wind. Both roe and buck shad were caught in drift nets, although roe shad were particularly prized. Overfishing and the construction of the Conowingo Dam in 1928 brought an end to the industry.

Of the other two craft, the menhaden striker boat was also made redundant, although new technology in the form of a spotter aircraft was the cause. The menhaden steamer, with attendant purse boats and striker boat, was a common sight on the East Coast from the late 1800s to the 1960s. Menhaden fishing is still an important industry in Virginia's portion of the Chesapeake, although the striker boats and wooden purse boats are no more.

A lapstrake pilot's rowing gig completes the Chesapeake Bay Maritime Museum's collection of round-bilge boats. Craft like this have now been replaced by modern, power driven launches for use by Bay pilots.

Yankee Skiff (Staten Island Skiff)

Built circa 1890s, Vicinity of Staten Island,
New York
22' 6-1/8" x 6' 2"

Henry Hall, in his 1884 report on shipbuilding, observed that several builders in the Staten Island – Raritan Bay area were making these oyster skiffs in three sizes – 18, 19 and 20 feet (measured on the bottom). Frames were made from the roots of white oak trees. Characteristics included a slightly rockered bottom, raking transom, and a box keel tapering at each end.

This 18-foot example (18 feet on the bottom) has naturally shaped frames and is lapstrake planked in white cedar. Similar skiffs exist in the collections of The Mariners' Museum, Mystic Seaport Museum and the Staten Island Historical Society.

Hundreds of these craft were brought down from the north on the decks of schooners to the Lower Chesapeake, particularly to the York River. Some also found their way to Maryland waters, as evidenced in a picture in the first edition of Elias Jones' *History of Dorchester County*, which shows a fleet of tonging boats including a Yankee skiff. The lines of one of these boats were taken off and drawn up by Martin Erismann, and appeared in *Forest and Stream* magazine in 1906.

This particular example was owned by John T. Gage of Dandy, York County, Virginia, who, at age 14, started oystering in the boat with his father.

The graceful craft provided a stable platform from which to tong oysters. A ceiling inside the boat made it easier to shovel oysters and prevented wear and tear on the bottom. Forward are two pairs of tholepins. Neither sailing rig nor engine was ever fitted, although they were in some skiffs.

Purchase

68-116-1

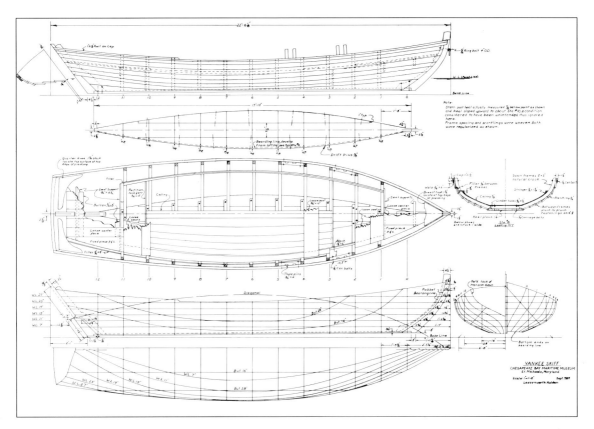

John T. Gage standing on the culling board of his Yankee skiff.

Gilling skiffs for hire at Betterton, Maryland.

Gilling Skiff (Shad Skiff)

Date and place of build unknown
24' 11" x 7' 7-1/2"

Little is known about the background of this boat, which is one of two gilling skiffs (shad skiffs) in the collection. She was one of a number of gilling skiffs once used in the prolific Susquehanna River fishery and was probably built to a standard design. Older rowing skiffs were converted to power in the early 20th century, or, like this model, were originally built for power. Her stern is of the later fuller type, developed to offset the squat produced by power.

This skiff is built of cedar on steam bent frames, 12 inches on center with white oak sheer strake, transom and keel. All planking is butted on frames. When received, numerous frames had been removed for replacement; the hull had been strapped together to retain its shape. Like other gilling skiffs, there is a prominent mooring bitt in the bow, made from the top part of the stem. She remains in an unrestored state.

Donor: Carroll Clarke

70-76-1

Gilling skiff (CBMM 70-76-1) as found in 1970.

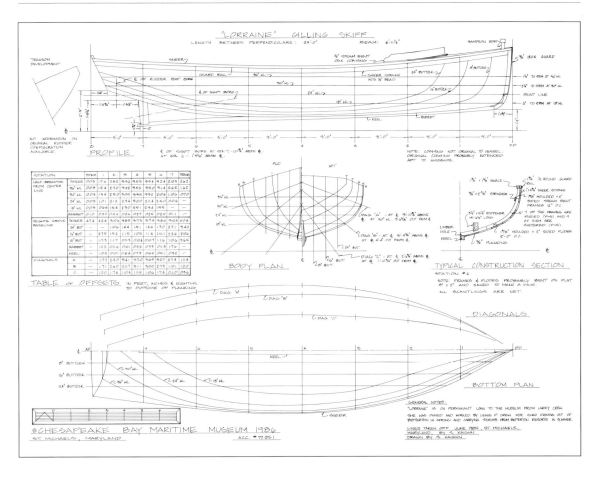

Lorraine
Gilling Skiff (Shad Skiff)

Date and place of build unknown
24' 0" x 6' 11-1/4"

*L*orraine once belonged to Lewis P. Crew of Betterton, a veteran of 50 years of gillnet fishing. During the summer *Lorraine* was hired out to excursionists at the resort of Betterton on Maryland's Eastern Shore, at the going rate of two dollars an hour. Early 20th-century postcards often showed these skiffs tied up at Betterton piers. The use of gilling skiffs for fishing was mainly confined to the Upper Bay.

Lorraine was built for an inboard engine in the early 1900s. She does not have the fine wine glass stern of earlier sailing models. She is constructed of white cedar on bent and sawn oak frames set on 12-inch centers. A large curved thwart aft enabled the net to be carried and boated from the stern. A pair of oarlocks was set far forward for maneuvering the boat under oars when working the net. A graceful curved coaming is fastened to the foredeck and extends part way aft.

Lorraine, **on exhibit in the Museum's Small Boat Shed.**

On Loan from Larry Crew

77-25-1

Striker Boat on display in 1990.

Striker Boat

Date of build unknown,
Probably at Reedville, Virginia
11' 10" x 4' 10-1/2"

The functional and sturdy striker boat was once a common feature in the Atlantic Coast purse seine fishery and survived into the 1960s. This particular example was owned by the Fish Products Company of Lewes, Delaware, before its donation to the Museum. The boat was probably built at the company's own shipyard in Reedville, Virginia, which closed in 1973.

A 600-foot purse net was used to catch menhaden. Once a school was sighted, the striker boat with its lone oarsman was sent to the side of the school opposite the mother ship or "bunker boat". Two purse boats then laid out the net astern, circling the school at a signal from the striker boat. The man in the striker boat made sure that the fish did not escape the net by striking the water with an oar (hence the name). Once the net was closed he "pulled the corks" of the bunt (the baggy mid-section of the net) to keep fish from going over the top, then dropped the "tom," a heavy weight that pulled the bottom of the net together, trapping the fish.

The skiff is constructed of cedar planks on steam bent frames with oak sheer strakes and clamps. No rudder is fitted but a slot is cut for a sculling oar. Two pairs of oarlocks are also fitted. Large lifting rings are attached to the stem and stern posts for hoisting on to the mother ship. In the foresheets are four holes where pegs were fitted to temporarily hold a portion of the net. Striker boats are not used in today's purse seine fishery, having been replaced by the spotter aircraft.

Donor: Fish Products Company, Lewes, Delaware

74-15-1

Gig similar to one in the Museum's collection being used by the Association of Maryland Pilots.

Pilot's Gig

Built circa 1956, place of build unknown
17' 2-1/4" x 5' 6"

This sturdy but graceful lapstrake gig was designed by Annapolis naval architect George E. Meese for use by the Association of Maryland Pilots. She was used to row pilots between their steamers and vessels entering or leaving the Chesapeake and had to withstand the rough seas often found at the mouth of the Bay.

The gig is equipped with three pairs of oarlocks with corresponding thwarts. Fore and aft are two lifting rings for hoisting on deck. Ten white cedar planks are attached to steam bent frames by copper rivets. A wide rub rail with grooves for a rope fender (now missing) runs along the sheer.

Donor: Association of Maryland Pilots

71-34-1

Delaware on Broad Creek, Laurel, Delaware, sometime before 1929.

Delaware
Tug

Built 1912, Bethel, Delaware,
by William H. Smith
39' 8" x 11' 4"   Official No. 228566

Delaware is a product of Bethel's great age of wooden ship and boatbuilding at the beginning of the 19th century and, apart from the 1900 ram schooner *Victory Chimes* (formerly *Edwin and Maud*), may be the only survivor.

William H. Smith, a foreman at the Bethel Shipyard, built the small tug in a shed on the grounds of a cannery adjoining the shipyard. After her hull was completed, she was moved to the marine railway to have her gasoline engine installed and was then launched.

Delaware hauled scows on Broad Creek, often laden with lumber, and towed ram schooners to and from Laurel. Occasionally she carried parties of young people to Sandy Hill on the Nanticoke River for the day. A partition behind the engine (since removed) created a small cabin with two benches and a stove. Two berths for the crew were located below the pilothouse. Originally a brass engine telegraph system connected the pilothouse with the engine room. An early photograph of the tug shows she was painted white overall.

In 1929, the tug was bought by James Ireland of Easton, Maryland, who was in partnership with John H. Bailey in a marine construction business. Later Bailey acquired sole interest in the tug and she became a common sight around the Upper Eastern Shore, engaged in building bulkheads and docks until she was laid up in the late 1980s.

Delaware went through a number of engines in her life and presently has a modified 671 GM diesel which was fitted by Crockett Bros. Boatyard in Oxford, Maryland, in 1947. New frames and bottom planking were also installed at this time. Her cabin, however, retains the original tongue and groove siding and sash windows.

Delaware is a rare example of a typical early 20th century wooden river tug. She will eventually be restored to her 1912 appearance.

Donor: Bailey Marine Construction, Inc.

91-3-1

V-BOTTOM BOATS

V-bottom boats are by far the most common type of craft to be found on the Chesapeake Bay, yet this has been a relatively recent development. The construction of V-bottom hulls on the Chesapeake dates to the 1880s, not long after the appearance of flat-bottom workboats.

The V-bottom, or hard chine hull, is an improvement on the flat-bottom model, allowing greater seaworthiness and carrying capacity. Its origins lay in the Long Island Sound area with the development of the "Northern skipjack" after the Civil War. Although this construction method, according to Howard I. Chapelle in *American Small Sailing Craft*, was imported from the north, the Chesapeake rapidly became the home of V-bottoms.

On the Chesapeake, in recent years, any V-bottom hull with a hard chine is generally called a "deadrise." The term "deadrise" refers to the angle formed by the bottom of the boat as it projects outward and upward from the keel at the rabbet line towards the outer edges of the chine; the smaller the angle the less the deadrise.

Captain Ed Leatherbury

Probably the most numerous deadrise sailing craft were the large class of skiffs commonly called crabbing skiffs. In a two-part article in *Yachting* (June and October 1943), later reprinted by the Chesapeake Bay Maritime Museum, Howard I. Chapelle identified 14 varieties of crabbing skiffs found along the lower Eastern Shore of Maryland. This constitutes only a partial list of the different types once known on the Chesapeake. In this work, Chapelle described crabbing skiffs from Cambridge, Taylor's Island, Hooper Island, Smith Island, Deal Island, and Wingate, among others. In his conclusions, he noted the suitability of the designs to specific local conditions, such as winds, shoals, and crabbing methods. These skiffs typically carried a single mast and sprit rig and in some areas were locally known as "dinky skiffs."

Deadrise sailing craft much over 20 feet were usually referred to as "bateaux." Like many terms applied to Chesapeake craft, no one is sure how this description came to be applied. It may have been brought to the region by the French Acadians who were transported to Maryland during the French and Indian Wars of the mid-1700s. Whatever its origin, the term bateau was later used to describe any large V-bottom boat, whether sail or power.

Smaller bateaux appeared first, and by the late 1880s larger ones were being built capable of pulling two oyster "scrapes," small dredges used in shallow rivers and bays.

A type of bateau that gained widespread popularity in the Tangier Sound area in the late 19th century was the barcat, sometimes called a "scrape", or "Jenkins Creeker," after the area near Crisfield where the type reportedly developed. This craft is remarkable for its low freeboard, shoal draft, sweeping sheer and wide beam, and is represented in the collection by *Shorebird*. Boats like her arose in response to the increased demand for soft crabs which are caught by means of scrapes, small dredges with no teeth. L. Cooper Dize of Crisfield patented the crab scrape in 1870. These graceful boats are still actively worked, under power, near Smith and Tangier Islands.

Larger in scale are the two-sail bateaux or skipjacks. It was a natural step from the smaller bateau used for oyster scraping to the larger version that was powerful enough to haul two full-size oyster dredges over a "rock" or oyster bed. The oldest known cross-planked dredging bateau was the *Ruby G. Ford*, built in 1891 in Fairmount, Maryland.

The next two decades would see a remarkable increase in the number of two-sail bateaux as they began to supplant the older bugeyes, sloops and schooners in the dredging fleet. These craft were usually distinguished by a single mast (although some three-sail bateaux were built with two masts) with a long-footed main and jib. Today the term "skipjack" is more commonly used to refer to a vessel with a leg-of-mutton mainsail and jib and a hard-chine hull. In 1990-1991 about fifteen skipjacks were dredging oysters on the Chesapeake.

The rapid spread of the bateau, and its survival on the Chesapeake through the conversion to power and to the present day is attributable to its simple and economical design. Most of the bateaux on the Bay are cross-planked on the bottom, with the planks sweeping aft on a diagonal from the keel to the chine, forming a herringbone pattern. These planks are typically heavy enough to lend sufficient athwartships strength to the hull without the use of bottom frames. Sufficient longitudinal strength is supplied by the heavy keelson normally found in these boats. Additional stiffening was provided by fitting several strongbacks, running from chine to chine. In the case of larger sailing bateaux, tie rods were also added, running from one side to the other.

The absence of bottom frames (except for a longitudinal stringer midway between the keel and chine on the larger bateaux) reduces the labor and materials involved in the construction of the hull, which makes the boat less expensive. It also simplifies construction, allowing many watermen to build their own boats.

V-bottom boats on the Chesapeake are characterized by their shoal draft and moderate deadrise. The chine in a powerboat typically rests slightly below the waterline and is flat through most of its run, rising only slightly forward. In sailing craft, on the other hand, the chine sweeps upwards at the stern, substantially above the waterline in some cases. The stem is generally plumb or raked slightly forward, and the stem post is almost invariably straight. A variety of stern designs may be found on the V-bottom workboats, most of which made their appearance with the advent of power-driven craft. The older sailing craft generally carried a transom that raked aft, meeting the herringbone-planked bottom above the waterline at the chine and slightly below at the keel.

On most of the larger sailing bateaux the rudder was carried outboard although some were built with inboard rudder posts. Closely related to the shoal-draft hull form is the use of the centerboard in place of a fixed keel. Bay sailing craft of every length have predominantly employed centerboards since the 19th century, from the smallest crabbing skiffs to the large two-sail bateaux built for oyster dredging.

With the availability of engines for workboats at the beginning of this century, at first sailboat hulls and hull forms were adapted to power, but later, several workboats appeared that were designed expressly for power.

Rosie Parks *on the* Miles River, *1989*.

The variety of power workboat designs is best exhibited by their sterns. Geography had much to do with design. In Virginia, a deadrise workboat was developed that had a high bow, sweeping sheer and round stern. Another rarer type has a wedge-shaped stern, possibly designed to emulate the sea-keeping qualities of the double ended log canoe. In Maryland, the tuck-stern and diamond-stern styles were often preferred. The most common style seen today is the flat- or box-stern which may not be as good looking, but is easier to make and provides a wider work platform aft. The box-stern is also less prone to squatting at speed and, with twin screws, provides better steering qualities.

One of the most attractive and distinctive of all

deadrise workboats was undoubtedly the Hooper Island launch, also variously called a "ducktail," "draketail," or "torpedo stern." The Hooper Island launch was a long, narrow, light displacement and shoal draft workboat that had its origins in the early 20th century. Its most characteristic feature was its rounded fantail with reverse rake made by using vertical staving. With these craft, the chine followed the water line for nearly the full length of the run.

Local tradition credits its origin to early 20th century naval torpedo boat destroyers whose sterns had a similar reverse rake. Howard I. Chapelle, on the other hand, believed that the racing launch *Fairbanks No. 2* (built in Oxford, Maryland, in 1902), was the origin of the design. The half model of this boat, at the National Museum of American History, shows a close similarity to later Hooper Island launches. Chapelle also stated that plans and information for the launch *Dolphin*, which appeared in the November 1903 issue of *The Rudder*, influenced the design, although this craft had a wide transom stern.

Whatever the origin of the Hooper Island launch, it was among the earliest workboat designs to be developed exclusively for power. The hull, with a beam of less than one-sixth the length, was made for considerable speed with the one-cylinder Palmer and Lathrop engines in the early models. In the 1930s, converted automobile engines replaced the one-cylinder engines, and the beam was widened, but the Hooper Islanders never performed as well when so overpowered. At the higher speeds, they would squat in the stern, increasing their wave-making and correspondingly reducing their efficiency.

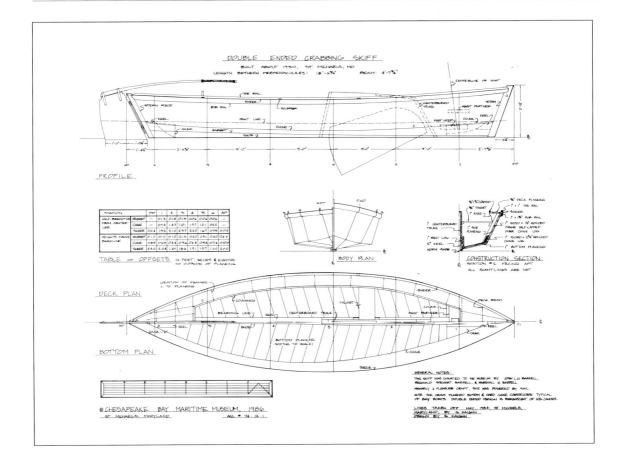

Double-Ended Sailing Skiff

Built circa 1929, St. Michaels, Maryland
18' 6-3/4" x 4' 7-3/4"

The builder of this solid and relatively narrow craft is unknown, but the hull form is not unlike that of a log canoe. The bottom is cross-planked in the typical herringbone pattern, and is fitted with a heavy keelson, chine logs and side frames. The bottom staving stops short of the stem post, where it would be too difficult to shape or twist the planks. In this space are three solid head blocks carved to the desired shape, and running parallel to the keelson. This skiff draws about 10 inches with the centerboard raised.

The rudder presently has a tiller mounted on top, but this was probably not used when the skiff was a workboat, as it would have taken up cockpit space. The rudder has small notches on top that may have held a yoke, so steering cables could be rigged along each side on the washboards.

This skiff evidently always carried a one-masted rig and was never converted to power. Her unstayed mast raked aft and carried a jib-headed main with a sprit and club. A short removable bowsprit held a forestay for a small, canoe-type jib. According to Fendall Marbury, who sailed the skiff for several summers, this jib and bowsprit often got in the way.

The boat is believed to have been built about 1929 in St. Michaels, but the date is uncertain. The original owner took the skiff to Turner's Creek, off the Sassafras River in Kent County. In 1932, she was purchased by the Barroll family and used for pleasure sailing until 1954, after which she was stored in a barn. Under their ownership the boat sailed to Norfolk, and made numerous evening trips to the dancing pavilion in Betterton.

Donors: John L. W. Barroll,
Reginald Stewart Barroll, and Marshall M. Barroll

74-12-1

Double-ended sailing skiff at CBMM, 1986.

Double-ended sailing skiff after being dismasted in Turner's Creek, 1941. Fendall Marbury, Sr. in stern, Lewin Wethered in bow.

Circa 1920 crabbing skiff was powered first by engine and later by poling.

Crabbing Skiff

Built circa 1920, place unknown
18' 9-3/4" x 4' 5"

The history of this boat is known only from 1938, when it was purchased from Homer Cannon of Crocheron, Dorchester County, by James R. Mills of Cornersville, Maryland. Mills, the maternal grandfather of Jackson R. Todd, took his young grandsons aboard the skiff while crabbing and oystering and, as they grew older, they assisted with the work. Mills made his living with this skiff for 20 to 30 years while raising his three grandsons.

The boat was powered with a Palmer engine when Mills acquired it. When the engine wore out, he had it removed and propelled the boat with only a push pole. The skiff evidently never carried a sailing rig. It is of a type once frequently used on the grassy shallows of Tangier Sound to catch soft crabs.

This craft is sometimes referred to as a Smith Island crabbing skiff, and in some places, a dinky skiff. Unlike most other Chesapeake V-bottoms, it is planked fore and aft on widely spaced sawn frames. There is no keelson, chine log, or other longitudinal framing. The fore-and-aft planking gives the boat a fairer bottom than most of the cross-planked skiffs, but this model and construction, according to Howard I. Chapelle in *Chesapeake Bay Crabbing Skiffs*, was limited to boats under 20 feet in length.

Donors: Mr. and Mrs. Jackson R. Todd

72-31-1

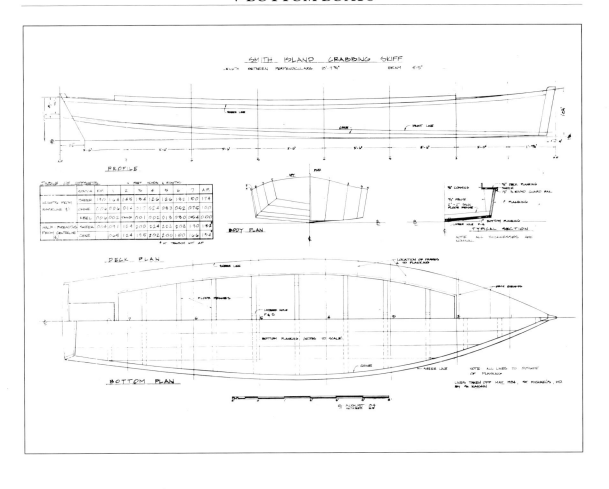

SMITH ISLAND CRABBING SKIFF

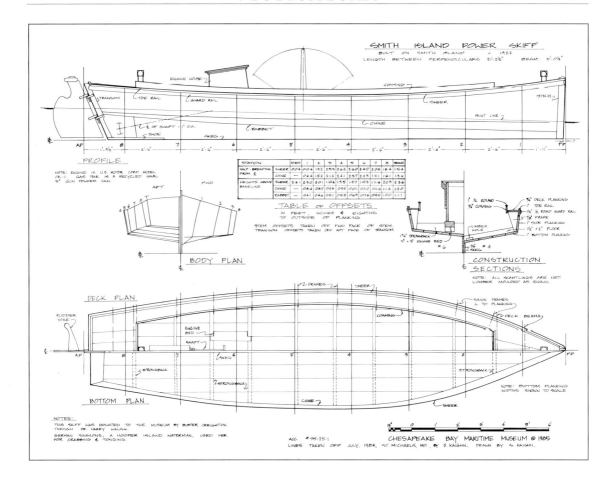

Smith Island
Power Crabbing Skiff

Built circa 1923-1924, Smith Island, Maryland
21' 2-1/2" x 5' 0-1/2"

Although built for mechanical power, this skiff has a hull form developed for use under sail. The boat came to the Museum with a one-cylinder Falcon engine, but, owing to its advanced state of deterioration, the engine has since been replaced with a one-cylinder Regal gasoline engine, which dates to about 1920.

Hooper Island waterman Gorman Simmons bought the skiff from a man at Wingate, who in turn had bought the boat on Smith Island. Simmons' son, Victor, remembers helping his father install the gas tank, a re-used five-inch naval gunpowder can that floated ashore on Hooper Island from the naval gunnery range at Barren Island during the Second World War. Because the skiff floated fairly low in the water, Gorman Simmons added an eight-inch high coaming inside the original coaming to make the craft dryer and to increase its carrying capacity. This additional coaming has been removed to restore the boat nearer to her original appearance.

Gorman Simmons used this craft mostly in the summer when trotlining for crabs. When he went oyster tonging in the winter, he towed a skiff behind this boat to carry oysters, as he did not wish to damage the bottom of his boat.

In 1970, Gorman Simmons gave his "Smith Islander" to his neighbor, Milford "Eagle" Creighton, a carpenter and mechanic. Creighton never used the skiff, and it rested in a field for years until he gave it to his friend Dr. Harry Walsh.

Like others of its type, she is shallow draft and fore-and-aft planked. The stem is nearly plumb,

Smith Island Power Crabbing Skiff.

with a straight rabbet. The forefoot is carved out of three chunks laid together. These chunks were typically attached with treenails carved to shape. Then drift pins were driven in to replace the treenails.

These craft were commonly used for crabbing and oyster tonging on Tangier Sound. This skiff has no keelson or chine log, although a keel and skeg are fixed to the underside of the hull.

Donors: Milford Creighton/Dr. Harry M. Walsh

75-25-1

Sailing Skiff

Built circa 1928,
probably at Oxford, Maryland, by Curtis Applegarth
17' 11" x 5' 9"

This graceful skiff was reportedly built by Curtis Applegarth, who started building boats at Cambridge, Maryland, in the early 1920s. He later established a yard in Oxford, Maryland, where he became known as a builder of small skipjacks.

He built this skiff for a man in southern New Jersey. After being stored in a barn at May's Landing, New Jersey, she was acquired by the former Down Jersey Marine Historical Society. In 1981 the skiff was transferred to the Philadelphia Maritime Museum, before coming to the Chesapeake Bay Maritime Museum.

The skiff is heavily built of yellow pine, with moderate deadrise amidships, increasing at both ends. The chine meets the stem at the waterline, dips a little amidships, and rises sharply out of the water at the stern. She is planked in a herringbone fashion, typical of Chesapeake Bay V-bottom construction. Each chine log is spliced together in two places.

The stem is nearly plumb and is made of two pieces, and the transom rakes aft and meets the waterline at the base of its vee. The rudder is hung outboard and is attached to a small false sternpost. A hewn keelson follows the shape of the bottom, and a small skeg of heavy construction extends below it at the stern.

This skiff has relatively narrow washboards for a Chesapeake Bay craft. A monkey rail is fitted atop the sheer strake and ends at the horse in the middle of the transom. The cockpit is large and the centerboard trunk is free-standing, not braced with a thwart. Her mast is set well forward and carried a sloop rig.

Exchange
81-11-1

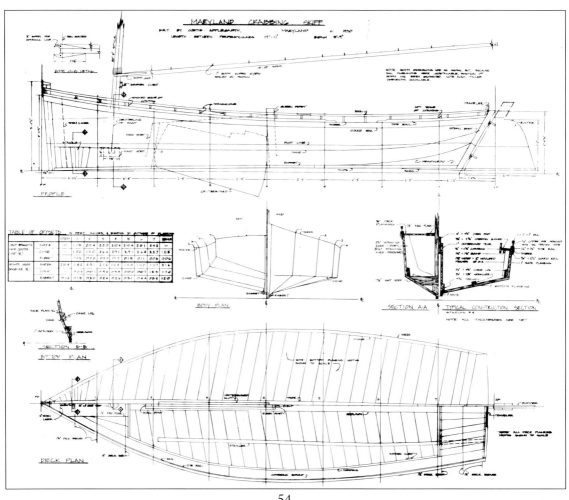

Ava
Sailing Skiff

Built circa 1930, Shadyside, Maryland,
by Capt. Charles Edward Leatherbury
11' 10-1/2" x 5' 5"

Ava before acquisition by CBMM in 1978.

C aptain Ed Leatherbury (1863-1952) built
boats behind his house on West River, near
Shadyside (see CBMM 66-22-1). At one time he
kept a 46-foot buyboat, *Juheru*, at the nearby
steamboat pier after the steamboats stopped
running to Shadyside. *Juheru* burned on 13
December 1937 with a load of gasoline aboard
and, soon after, Leatherbury began to build a fleet
of skiffs. As he got too old to go fishing and
oystering himself, he chartered these skiffs out by
the hour or the day, which left him time for

boatbuilding. The skiffs were slightly varied in
design, and ranged from 14 to 20 feet in length.
Each had its name on small plaques attached to
each side of the bow: *Ava, Jay, Bob, Fey, Teal,
Lou, Cap,* and others.

Each of the skiffs was cross-planked with slight
deadrise. They had pine masts and booms, and
metal fish net rings replaced the wooden mast
hoops.

The fleet was sold in the late 1940s to Richard
Hartge but continued to be chartered out. Several
were sold privately, and in 1961, Mr. and Mrs. Ken
Smith bought the remaining nine skiffs.
Although they continued to hire them out, they
sold off *Teal* and *Ava*.

On *Ava*, the rudder and forward part of the
rudder post are hewn from a tree limb, and the
main sheet is fastened through a hole in the top of
the post. *Ava* is rigged with a single sail, the mast
set well forward, catboat fashion. The deck is
strip-planked. A similar skiff can be seen in the
collection of the Calvert Marine Museum.

Donor: Mrs. Ray Brown
78-34-1

Six Leatherbury skiffs at Galesville, Maryland.

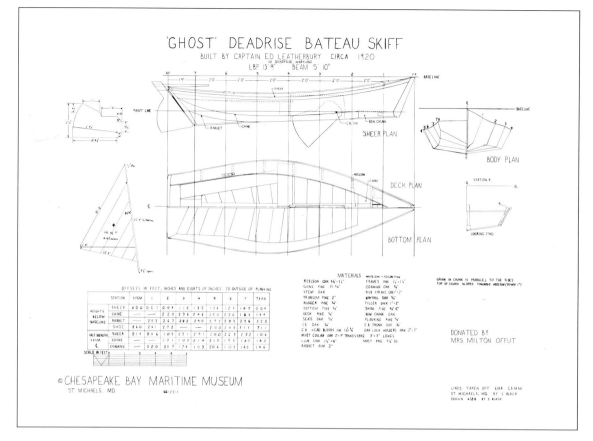

Ghost
Deadrise Skiff

Built circa 1916-1920, Shadyside, Maryland,
by Capt. Charles Edward Leatherbury
15' 9" x 5' 10"

Captain Ed Leatherbury was a well-known West River builder of bateaux, skiffs, and log canoes (see CBMM 78-34-1). He built boats during the winter in a shed on the back of his property that he rented to boarders in the summer. Nearby was his small marine railway, operated with only a block and tackle, not an engine.

Ghost was acquired by Milton Offutt in the mid-1920s and berthed at his home on Gunbottom Creek, off the Severn River, where it was sailed extensively until the Second World War. Milton Offutt purchased the 53-foot skipjack-rigged, frame-built bugeye *Richard J. Vetra* in 1934. In 1937 or 1938 she was converted to a bugeye rig, and travelled to log canoe races and other regattas with canoes *Magic, Island Bird,* and *Ghost* in tow. After *Vetra* was sold in 1942, *Ghost* was pulled up on shore and never sailed again.

Ghost carried a single 146-square-foot leg-of-mutton sail on a raked mast. She is planked and decked in yellow pine, with frames. Most of her other structural members are made of white oak. As is sometimes seen on the Chesapeake, the forefoot is made up of "chunks" with the grain parallel to the herringbone planking. This skiff has a particularly sharp deadrise increasing at the bow and stern.

Ghost before her donation in 1966.

Donor: Mrs. Milton Offutt

66-22-1

Ghost on exhibit.

Bessie Lee
Seaside Bateau

Built circa 1920, Townsend, Virginia,
by John Hanson Downes
18' 4" x 7' 1"

Bessie Lee being restored, 1985. Clearly visible are the three forward mast partners.

The seaside bateau is indigenous to the Eastern Shore of Virginia, and was designed for sailing through the inlets and narrow, winding channels between barrier islands and marshes on the Atlantic coast. The wide flare at the bow throws off the surf in these rough waters. Seaside bateaux were deadrise boats, but a round bilge version with the same dimensions was called a skiff. There were also smaller, 13-1/2-foot "sister" vessels to the seaside bateaux called "jiggers". The seaside bateaux were used for oystering, clamming, and net fishing.

The type is distinguished by its great flare, its wide washboards, and its unusual rig. *Bessie Lee* carries a two-stick rig, but there are three mast steps up forward in addition to the mainmast step. When the full rig is used, the foremast is stepped in the foremost hole. In heavier airs, the foremast is moved to the second step, and the main is removed. In still stronger breezes, the main alone is stepped in the aftermost of the three holes. Both sails are sprit-rigged, with a club at the clew of the fore but not on the main. The mainsheet leads through a sheave on an outrigger off the stern.

According to Howard I. Chapelle, who called the bateaux "Chincoteague Skiffs," the construction of these craft was typical of the Chesapeake Bay, except that there is only a plank keelson instead of a hewn log keelson, no strongbacks are present, and the construction is relatively light overall. According to Chapelle, this model appeared about 1905.

John Hanson Downes (born 4 March 1892), builder of *Bessie Lee*, was, like his father, a carpenter and boatbuilder. Today he and his father are better remembered as decoy carvers, as they spent all of their free time hunting the seaside marshes or fishing the nearby waters. Downes lived in Townsend, Virginia, where he built approximately six seaside bateaux. In nearby Magotha Bay, races were held in the 1920s and 1930s between these local craft. Older residents remember these races as one of the social highlights of the summer.

Bessie Lee is one of the few surviving examples of the seaside bateau.

Bessie Lee *in light airs.*

Donor: Clarence W. Strickland

82-14-1

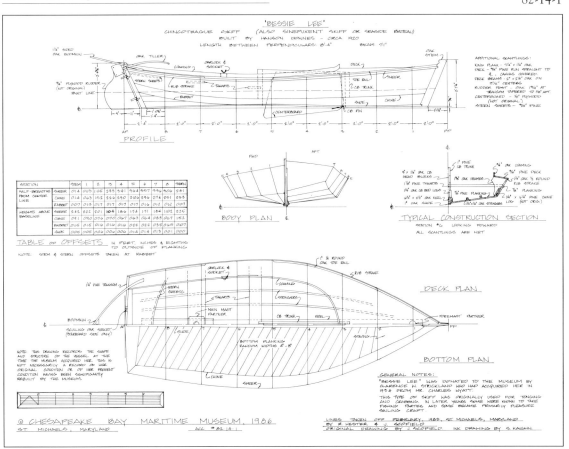

Lark
Sailing Skiff

Built circa 1918-1920, probably on West River,
Anne Arundel County, Maryland
20' 0" x 5' 10"

This sloop-rigged bateau is of the type that dates to the 1880s, a smaller cousin of the larger skipjack. *Lark* most likely was built with an inboard engine, as there is evidence of an engine mount and a bored shaft, since plugged. The sailing rig was evidently added after the hull was completed.

The hull is built of local pine, and the construction is similar to the larger skipjacks: herringbone planking, heavy keelson and chine logs, and no bottom frames. The model is narrower than working skiffs, but this boat was never used as a working crab skiff. The bateau originally had thwarts instead of the present U-shaped stern seats.

The rig consists of a mainsail and club-footed jib on a single unstayed mast. The mainsail is like that of the sailing log canoes, with a club at the clew held out by a sprit ("spreet"). The mainsail is furled around the club and wrapped to the mast, and the mast is generally unstepped when the boat is not sailing.

The boat was built for a Mr. Kerr, possibly the yacht captain Charles Kerr, of Rock Hall, Kent County, for pleasure sailing.

Donor: Roy P. Elbourn

69-74-1

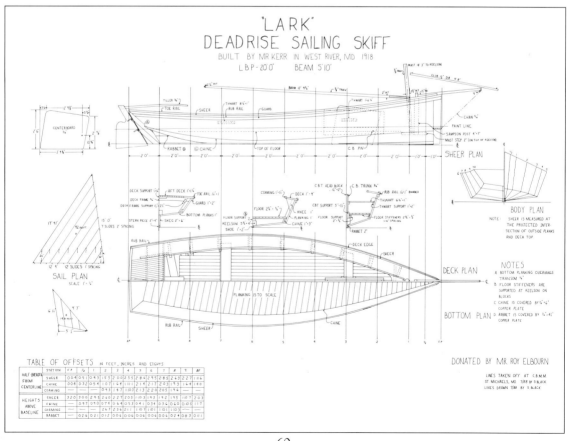

Potomac River Dory

Built 1929, River Springs, Maryland,
by Walter Cheseldine
33' 7" x 10'   Official No. 282620

One of the Museum's two Potomac River Dories (see CBMM 88-43-1) was built by well-known White's Neck boatbuilder, Walter Cheseldine, in St. Mary's County. She was designed as a sailing dory with the traditional two-masted, jib-headed rig. Dory sails were either sprit-rigged or laced to a conventional boom.

She was built for Elmer L. Ward of Dowell, Maryland, who used her for oystering and later for charter boat fishing. In her latter guise, she was motorized and had an extended cabin with canopy, replacing the traditional small cuddy cabin.

Ward documented the boat in 1960 and gave her the name *Thomas L. Ward* (Ward's son). Shortly after, however, she was sold and went through a succession of owners, mainly in the Annapolis area. She later acquired the name *Old Salt*. In 1990, the year she was donated, the boat was brought over to Maryland's Eastern Shore. When the Museum acquired the craft, she had been laid up and had lost her cabin and engine.

The former sailing dory still retains her centerboard slot and mast steps, and the long leaf yellow pine and cypress hull planking is original – a tribute to her builder and the careful attention Elmer Ward gave to the boat. In typical dory fashion, she is planked fore and aft, her side planking being of one piece from stem to stern. A feature rarely seen on the Bay is the copper-lined scuppers, two per side.

Although his boat survived, Walter Cheseldine's boatshop and marine railway in River Springs are

Sailing dory as she appeared as a motorized fishing charter boat.

gone. This distinctive dory is one of only a handful that have been preserved on the Chesapeake.

Donor: Skipjack Landing Marine Center

91-4-1

Potomac River sailing dory shortly after arrival at CBMM, 1991.

"Peg Leg" Hayden's Potomac River dory boat at Banks O'Dee.

Potomac River Dory

Built 1931, Cobb Island, Maryland,
by Francis Raymond "Peg Leg" Hayden
37' 10-1/2" x 12' 7"

P otomac River Dories were built in southern
Maryland on the Potomac River and used
primarily for oystering. These boats are
descendants of the Black Nancy, a type of small
(18 to 27 foot) and narrow Potomac River
workboat dating to before the Civil War.
According to Edwin Beitzell, Potomac River
historian, the Potomac River Dory was designed
by Grason Thompson and Charles G. Huseman,
both of St. Patrick's Creek, in 1875.

J. Richley Delahay of Compton, Maryland
bought the boat around 1938 in a sunken
condition and refitted her. Later he passed the
boat on to his sons, Kenneth and Ronald, who
used her for oyster tonging. Always called the "big
dory," she was one of the few of her type to be
fitted with wheel steering.

She is painted in traditional dory colors: green,
red and yellow stripes adorn the lapped sheer
strake, and the topsides and deck are white.
Arthur Puchetti bought the boat in 1972 and had
the cabin widened, raised and extended aft. She
was also given the name *African Queen*.

Like the other Potomac River Dories, this one is

Potomac River dory boat undergoing restoration, winter 1990-1991.

planked fore and aft, and the chine rises high
above the waterline at her bow. Towards the bow,
the sawn frames reach from the keel to the top of

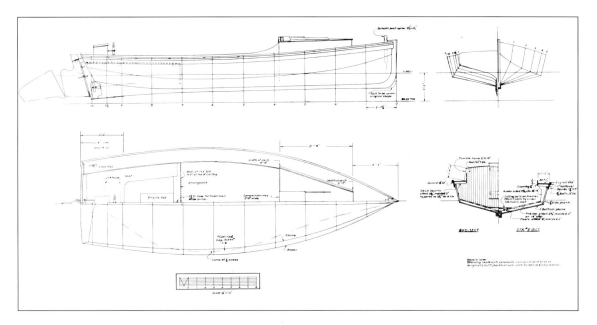

"Peg Leg" Hayden, builder of the 1931 Potomac River dory boat.

log. The frames are spaced at variable intervals. Her tuck stern and shield-shaped transom are typical of the Potomac River Dory. The bottom planks rise out of the water at the stern and the sharply raked transom only touches the water in the center. Washboards reach back to the transom, where there is a curved seat but no decking.

The boat is presently equipped with a six-cylinder Ford engine and two gas tanks. In the winter of 1990-1991 restoration commenced to bring her nearer to her original appearance.

Donor: Calvert Marine Museum

88-43-1

the side planks, stopping just short of the lapped sheer strake. Farther aft, the bottom frames are bolted to the side frames, but there is no chine

Shorebird in 1989 displays the low freeboard typical of crab scrapes.

Shorebird
Crab Scrape

Date and place of build unknown
24' 11-1/2" x 8' 4"

The sailing crab scrapes of Tangier Sound looked much like the larger oyster dredging bateaux, the "skipjacks," differing only in that these smaller craft were usually half-decked and had no permanent cabin trunk. The rig was also identical, except that the crab scrapes usually had no shrouds.

Shorebird has a straight keel line formed by the skeg, a graceful sheer, and the entrance is long, sharp and convex with a straight run amidships. A monkey rail is set atop pipe stanchions over a log rail. The hull is of yellow pine with white oak frames and deckbeams.

It is difficult to determine whether this bateau was originally powered or rigged, as she has undergone numerous changes. Sail generally went out of fashion in workboats after the First World War, and many of this type, typically 24 to 30 feet in length, were converted to power.

When Mr. and Mrs. Gene Russell acquired the boat in the mid-1980s she had been modified to carry a two-masted rig with bowsprit and large rudder. Shortly afterwards, she was restored by Eldon Willings, Jr. of Chance, Maryland, who converted her to a more traditional single-masted rig with a small cuddy cabin.

Although believed to have been built for sail, the lack of any evidence of a centerboard makes this uncertain. Large oil stains on the bottom planks, a plugged shaft bore and a strongback, now removed, indicate a long period of operation under inboard power. Her hull form, however, is very typical of Tangier Sound sailing crab scrapes, and may date to a time in the early 20th century when traditional hull forms were first adapted to the internal combustion engine.

Donors: Mr. and Mrs. Gene Russell

87-49-1

Minnie G. *on exhibit in 1984. Glass-enclosed wheelhouses, like the one fitted on* Minnie G., *were usually later additions.*

Minnie G.
Hooper Island Launch
Built circa 1926, probably at Middle Hooper Island, Dorchester County, Maryland, by Bronza Parks
36' 10" x 6' 5"

Minnie G. possesses the distinctive draketail stern of the Hooper Island launches, with its reverse rake.

She was built for Edwin Curtis Tyler of Hoopersville, Dorchester County, and was named for his wife, Minnie Gertrude Tyler. Edwin Curtis Tyler was the last civilian lighthouse keeper of the Hooper Strait Lighthouse before the Coast Guard took over, just prior to World War II. Minnie G. was his personal boat, which he used on his time off, and he occasionally used her to run out to the lighthouse.

The launch was later given to his son, Edwin Earl Tyler, who used the boat for fishing parties out of Solomons Island and, occasionally, Hooper Island during the summer. Minnie G. was also used for oyster tonging in the winter.

Minnie G. has pine sides on ash frames with a fir keel. Her bottom is diagonally planked with staving used at the bow. She has a fairly broad beam for her early construction and moderate flare. Minnie G. was said to be one of the fastest Hooper Island launches around.

When she came to the Museum, she was equipped with a six-cylinder converted Chevrolet engine of 120 horsepower.

Donor: William Owens

74-45-1

Bronza Parks, 1955

65

Martha
Hooper Island Launch

Built 1934, Wingate, Maryland, by Bronza Parks
43' 3-5/8" x 8' 3"   Official No. 233719

Named for Martha Lewis Glass, niece of Bronza Parks, and built for her brother, Paul Lewis, *Martha* was used for crabbing, oyster tonging, and pleasure.

Martha is a longer and beamier launch than *Minnie G.* (CBMM 74-45-1); it was typical in the later draketails to increase the beam to counter "squatting" in the stern when overpowered with the converted automobile engines available in the 1930s.

This elegant craft has a raised cabin forward, a small foredeck and afterdeck, and narrow washboards. Her flare increases toward the bow, and the stem has a gracefully curved rabbet. *Martha* has a heavy hewn keelson and longitudinal stringers running along the bottom planks, which are laid in herringbone fashion. A heavy strongback runs across her bottom at the forward end of the engine bed.

She came to the Museum with a 1971 V-8 Oldsmobile 455 engine of 360 horsepower. An uncharacteristic engine for the type, it was replaced with an in-line, six-cylinder Chevrolet. The engine, a model produced from 1958 to 1962, is cooled with a fresh water system.

Few draketail or ducktail launches are actively worked today, most having fallen victim to time and neglect. Those that are used for crabbing and oystering are mainly located in Dorchester County, on Maryland's Eastern Shore.

Donors: Mr. and Mrs. David W. Glass

83-19-1

Hooper Island launch Martha, in l983.

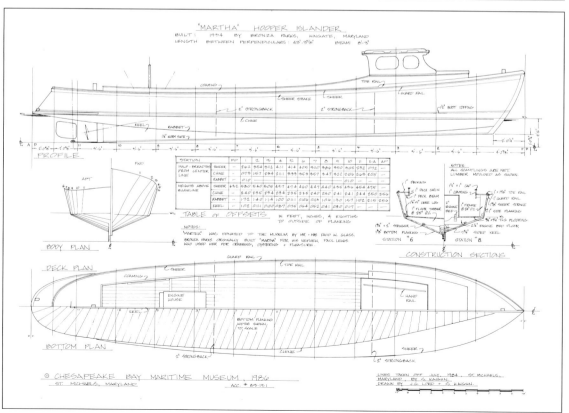

Shuttlecock
Utility Runabout

Built 1935, Newport News, Virginia,
by Horace E. Dodge Boat and Plane Corporation
16' x 5' 10"

S *huttlecock* is unique to this collection of watercraft in that she is the only one that was mass-produced to a standard design. She is a Dodge model 301 utility runabout, the smallest and most basic model produced by that company, costing $595 when new. Her hull number, 223, is marked on the stem, the dashboard plate and the engine box plate. Dodge was one of the earliest to adopt assembly line production for small pleasure boats.

The Dodge utility runabout is equipped with a four-cylinder, 45-horsepower Lycoming engine made by the Lycoming Manufacturing Company of Williamsport, Pennsylvania. Most models made by Dodge were equipped with Lycoming engines; the one in *Shuttlecock* is number UAB920C. It was rated to take the runabout up to speeds of 25 miles per hour. The original engine is still in the boat, and was restored in 1989-90, although it is not in running order.

The model 301 has a double-planked carvel bottom made of cedar on oak frames. The sides are of five lapped strakes with some tumblehome

towards the stern. *Shuttlecock* is an open runabout with a short foredeck and afterdeck and narrow washboards. Upholstered seats for the operator and six passengers were provided.

Shuttlecock's first owner was Isaac Potts of Baltimore. Remarkably she stayed in the Potts family until the 1980s.

Most of her original equipment has survived intact. Her original flagstaff was 1-1/2 inches taller, and she is missing her factory-installed combination running light with a mast socket for a triangular pennant, but all of her other fittings are present and appear to be original. The Museum restored *Shuttlecock* in 1990-1991.

Donors: Mr. and Mrs. Paul L. Warner

89-7-1

Dodge launch Shuttlecock *as received, 1989.*

Deadrise Sloop

Built 1929, Pot Pie (Wittman), Maryland,
by George Jackson
28' 1-7/8" x 7' 11-1/4"

The builder, George Jackson, lived not far from Kemp House, a boarding house near McDaniel, on the Eastern Shore of Maryland, where the artist Louis Feuchter sometimes stayed.

Feuchter commissioned the sloop for his own use, to be fitted with a small cruising cabin, a self-draining cockpit, a forehatch, and tiller steering.

After George Jackson launched the hull in April 1929, Feuchter had the boat towed to Brice's Boatyard at Spring Gardens, Baltimore, because the artist was living in the city at that time. There, Louis Feuchter rigged the craft himself. He later added a bracket for an outboard motor on the stern.

Although he intended to use the boat for cruising to the Eastern Shore of Maryland, his longest trip in the yacht took him to Wall Cove on Rock Creek, about 10 miles from his mooring. When he found that he was using the boat less, and that the maintenance was becoming a burden, he decided to sell the boat to his friend, Fred Broening, in the spring of 1951.

After Broening several later owners made changes in rigging details, the cabin arrangement, and some structural members. Most of the planking, the remaining portion of the bow chunk, the decking, and most of the transom are original, as is the masthead fitting. The color scheme is also original: brown sheer strake, green on the cabin top, and white elsewhere. When Feuchter owned the boat, there was a bulkhead between the cabin and the forehold, which is now removed. A bunk was fitted on either side of the cabin.

Eventually, the boat is to be restored to its appearance when owned by Louis Feuchter. It was from this craft that Feuchter sketched and painted many long-vanished Chesapeake sailing craft.

Donor: Godfrey R. Gauld

89-19-1

Louis J. Feuchter at the helm of his boat at Spring Gardens, Baltimore, 1935.

Burgess, Robert H. *Louis J. Feuchter–Chesapeake Bay Artist.* Newport News, VA: The Mariners Museum, 1976.

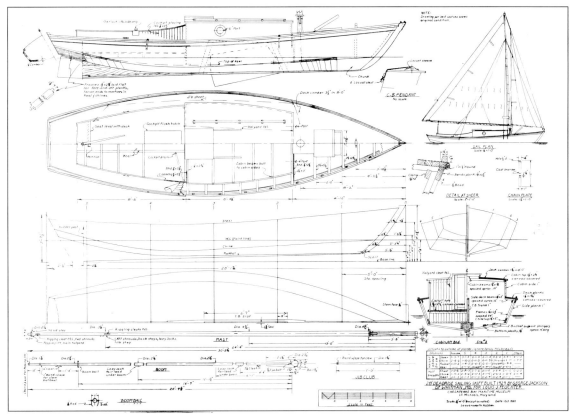

Deadrise sloop, shortly after arrival at CBMM, 1989.

Rosie Parks
Two Sail Bateau (Skipjack)

Built 1955, Wingate, Maryland, by Bronza Parks
51' x 16' 7"   Official No. 270542

This fast oyster-dredging bateau or skipjack was built in 1955 along with two sisters, *Martha Lewis* and *Lady Katie*. These were the last dredging bateaux built by Bronza Parks of Wingate, who died in 1958. She was built for the builder's brother, Captain Orville H. Parks, and named for their mother. Orville Parks was the only owner of the bateau before she came to the Museum. Captain Parks started oystering at the age of eleven and dredged for 68 consecutive seasons before bad health forced him to stop in December 1974. Under his command, *Rosie* was considered the fastest and best-captained skipjack in the fleet. She won first place many times in the annual Chesapeake Appreciation Days and Deal Island Workboat Races.

Rosie Parks was also considered the best-maintained skipjack on the Bay; she was hauled out annually by James Richardson of Lloyds, Maryland.

Rosie Parks has a generous amount of deadrise and a heavily rolled chine. Her keelson runs the full length and is framed by two sister keelsons. Her bow is fully staved and has no log filler. The bateau's knees, gussets, chine liner, and the planking for her centerboard well and bottom are fastened to heavy scantlings of loblolly pine and some fir. Side frames are of oak, with a mast of western fir, and she is fastened with galvanized iron spikes and riveted rods. Brass sheathing, for protection against ice, is fastened with silicon bronze.

She is still sailed actively by the Museum, but no longer carries her oyster dredging gear. Like all of the oyster dredging fleet, the boat does not have an inboard engine, but carries a pushboat slung in davits at the stern. Interestingly, *Rosie Parks* and her two sisters were built one-quarter mile away from the water, in a large lot adjoining Bronza Parks's home. They had to be hauled by cart to the water to be launched.

Purchase

75-53-1

Rosie Parks, *Martha Lewis* and *Lady Katie under construction, 1955. Note the large wheeled carts under the bow of* Martha Lewis, *used to haul the boats to water, a quarter-mile away.*

Captain Orville Parks at the wheel of Rosie Parks.

Burgess, Robert H. "Keeping Alive the Age of Sail–Bronza M. Parks, of Dorchester County, is Still Building Skipjacks for Maryland Oyster Dredgers." *Sun* (Baltimore) 8 Jan. l955.

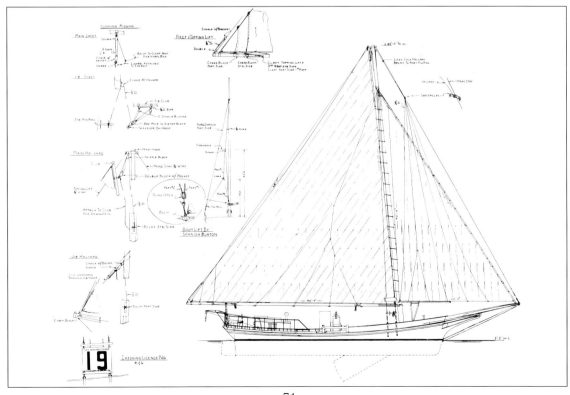

FLAT-BOTTOM BOATS

The use of flat-bottom boats on the Chesapeake can be traced back to the first settlements. However, flat-bottom construction in Bay oystering and crabbing craft did not appear until the 1880s, where previously only log canoes had served. Flat-bottom construction has two distinct advantages: it is the simplest to build as it requires fewer tools and fewer hours to construct than any other type of hull form for any given length. Additionally, it is especially suited to protected, shoal draft water, which is typical of the Chesapeake Bay.

Naval architect and historian Howard I. Chapelle classified flat-bottom boats into three categories: scows, punts, and skiffs (sharpies). The scow is the simplest and cheapest of the three to build; it is little more than a modified box, with its narrowed ends sweeping up from the bottom and little or no flare. The punt is a refinement of the scow, with a well-rockered bottom fore-and-aft, flaring sides, and a raking bow and transom. Skiffs have a pointed bow with less rocker forward than a punt, and sharpies are enlarged versions of the skiff, occasionally sporting a sharp or round stern.

Miles River yacht designer and builder, C. Lowndes Johnson, aboard his ketch, White Cap II.

The flat-bottom boat preceded the V-bottom on the Chesapeake. Scows were used in the colonial period for transporting tobacco. Flat-bottom sloops and schooners could be found before the advent of the skipjack; these boats were frequently used to transport lumber, grain, or other cargo around the Bay.

Howard I. Chapelle, in *The Migrations of an American Boat Type* (1963), restated the tradition that a New Haven sharpie named *Frolic* was found adrift on the Bay near Tangier Island, and was copied locally. Whether this had much impact on the development of flat-bottomed skiffs on the Bay is not known, but a number of them were in use by the 1880s in the crabbing industry. By the late 1880s and early 1890s they were rapidly replaced by V-bottoms in most areas. These boats typically carried a leg-of-mutton rig on two masts, although a half-decked variation was found at Smith Island, Crisfield, and Deal Island that carried a jib and mainsail rig.

The flat-bottom craft in this chapter can be divided into three categories by usage. The first category includes three boats used for fishing – two for shad fishing with gill nets, and a third for pound-net fishing. The second type is a pushboat, a small vessel that provided auxiliary power to oyster dredgeboats, which were not permitted by Maryland law to carry an inboard engine. The remaining three, all built by Lowndes Johnson(1881-1971) of Easton, Maryland, were yacht tenders and small pleasure craft.

Pound-net fishing began in Maryland in 1858 and was slow to find success, but by 1920 68 percent of the annual fish harvest in Maryland was caught with pound nets. A pound net consists of a floored net area, the pound head, and an elaborate system of nets designed to lead fish into the pound head, all supported on stakes driven into the shallow Bay bottom. In the collection is a double-ended craft designed to tend these nets, set in waters up to 15 or 20 feet deep. At low tide, the nets were slackened to allow the boat to pass inside the pound head. Once inside, the crew would pull up the floor of the pound head, working all the fish over to one side and raising them up so they could be scooped into the boat with large dip nets. At one time, pound nets could be found throughout the Bay, and their placement was regulated because they became hazards to navigation. Today, pound-net fishing has almost disappeared because of the expense of setting up and tending the nets, and the decline in the fish population.

The boats built for shad fishing come from the Choptank and Nanticoke Rivers. Those built in Sharptown and used on the Nanticoke are known as "Sharptown Barges." Though not geographically distant and sharing many characteristics with the Sharptown Barge, the Choptank River Shad Skiffs were never given the name "barge." The Sharptown Barges are longer than their counterparts on the Choptank and averaged around 22-24 feet. The length of the boats was determined by the depth of the nets used by the shad fishermen, which, in turn, was determined in part by the depth of the waters in which they generally worked.

The Sharptown Barge is a particularly remarkable sailing craft for the absence of a centerboard, leeboard, or keel. Without any such device to supply lateral resistance, these shoal draft boats could not sail upwind. It seems that the watermen who used these boats never did sail them upwind, but rowed or poled them when moving upwind. The rig was reserved for downwind work. With the mast stepped far forward and without any centerboard trunk, thwarts, or seats, the Sharptown Barge offered a long, clear space for handling the nets.

The Sharptown Barge was operated by two men, one in the bow, the other in the stern. To maneuver the craft, the man in the bow pushed an oar on one side of the boat while facing forward, and the other paddled and steered from the stern. To handle the net, one would pay out or haul in the top of the net to which floats were tied, and the other held the bottom. Barges were also used to tend muskrat traps, and were occasionally used as gunning guide boats.

John Goslee, a builder of many Sharptown Barges, believes the early examples were double-ended, but a transom stern was developed to provide more room in the stern and on which to fit an outboard engine.

Most flat-bottom workboats are cross-planked. This simplified construction and made frames unnecessary across the bottom of the boat, as the planks lent the requisite strength athwartships. This absence of frames across the bottom of the boat provided a smooth working and walking surface without the addition of a ceiling. Cross-planking was generally favored for flat-bottom boats on the Chesapeake, especially in workboats. The Homer Fletcher Sharptown Barge is an exception to this generalization, and can be accounted for by his professional boatbuilding background.

None of the three small flat-bottom craft built by Lowndes Johnson were workboats, and two of them are planked fore and aft. This construction is more difficult than cross-planked bottoms and requires full sawn frames. One is the pram named *Decoy*, a tender to Lowndes Johnson's cruising yacht *Whitecap II*. The other, *Widgeon*, is a sailing skiff that Johnson built for his own use to the modified design of a sailing rowboat his family had long owned. The original rowboat was evidently of the same type of construction, with fore-and-aft bottom planking.

The name "flat-bottom" can be misleading. It implies a chine hull that is not a V-bottom. The pound-net boat has some deadrise at both the bow and stern, but it is flat-bottomed through most of its run and, hence, included in this category. Most of the boats in this chapter have some rocker; "flat-bottom" describes the cross section of the boat, not the profile. Lowndes Johnson's pram, *Decoy*, not only has some rocker fore and aft, but athwartships as well, and is more properly termed an arc-bottom. This type of hull, also seen on the dredgeboat *Stanley Norman*'s push boat, is a variation of the flat-bottom with flat sides, a rounded bottom and a hard chine. Another example of this type is the Star Boat, a one-design racing class; these boats perform better in light airs than true flat-bottoms.

Choptank River Shad Skiff

Built early 1930s, Hog Creek, Maryland,
by Anton "Tony" Worm
18' 9-1/2" x 5' 0-1/2"

Choptank River shad skiff on exhibit at CBMM, 1992.

This skiff was used to net shad, herring, rockfish, and perch on the Choptank River near Dover Bridge on Maryland's Eastern Shore. This is believed to be the last boat Tony Worm built of bald cypress and using traditional methods. In 1990 his house and boat shop still stood on the corner of New Town Road and Hog Creek Road. He and Melvin Engle used the shad skiff for a number of years working out of "Wings Landing," the Worm family's farm.

The boat was discovered along the shore of that farm by Dr. and Mrs. Doughty when they bought part of the farm in 1962. Their son used the boat for pleasure on the river and cut the stern off to accommodate a plywood transom with an engine mount.

This alteration has led to some controversy concerning the original shape of the stern. Members of the Doughty family remember the boat as a double-ender; they believe that about 15 to 18 inches of the stern was cut off to accommodate the transom. Melvin Engle, a longtime local fisherman, remembers a narrow transom approximately eight inches wide, as was common to the type.

Choptank River Shad Skiffs were initially sailed, and later powered with either inboard or outboard engines. According to the Doughty family, this skiff was poled, which would be typical for double-ended construction. Net fishing and the craft that were used have all but disappeared from the Choptank River today.

Donor: Dr. Robert Doughty

89-20-1

Sharptown Barge

Built 1930s, Sharptown, Maryland,
by Homer Fletcher
19' 6" x 4' 8"

Homer Fletcher Sharptown barge, 1989.

Homer Fletcher (1888-1983) started his apprenticeship at the Sharptown Marine Railway in 1909, and made his living building schooners and other large craft, during the early 20th-century shipbuilding boom in Sharptown. Later he built this boat for his own use, possibly the only Sharptown Barge he made. He seined from the boat for many years until his retirement.

This shad skiff is unusual among Sharptown Barges in that it is planked fore and aft. The planking is white cedar, caulked with cotton. The sides are largely made from one strake, the port side having a long strip patched in, possibly to repair a crack amidships. At some point, the hull was fiberglassed but, when acquired, this had mostly been removed. The large half-round rubbing strakes are of oak. Six pairs of natural crook frames are fitted.

This boat was intended mainly for use with an outboard motor, and the transom is protected by a metal plate.

Donor: Mrs. Audrey F. Fletcher

89-30-1

Homer Fletcher.

Friedel, Dennis. "Homer Fletcher, One of a Forgotten Breed."
Source unknown, 1981.

Sharptown Barge

Built 1979, Sharptown, Maryland,
by John Edward Goslee
22' 1-3/4" x 5' 2-1/4"

John Edward Goslee is probably the last living builder of Sharptown Barges, used primarily for shad fishing on the Nanticoke River. He built this barge for Maryland State Senator Robert P. Dean of Centreville, Maryland, a great collector of old farm machinery and traction engines. This craft was never used for its intended purpose before the Museum acquired it at auction.

John Goslee has built about 200 shad barges and other skiffs since 1937-1938 when, at the age of 12, he built his first boat. Goslee made several innovations in the design of the Sharptown Barge. He was the first Sharptown builder to use two planks in the side instead of one as large white cedar, his preferred material, became difficult to find. He was also the first to fit the transom with the grain running horizontally, so the swelling of the wood in the water would not force the sides out. John Goslee began the practice of cutting off the knees short of the bottom, so as not to inter-fere with bailing. In older barges, the stern seat was a flat, removable board, but Goslee attached these seats permanently and at an angle.

The boat is planked with 3/4-inch white cedar and represents a later style of Goslee barges. The stem is of red cedar and the transom is black walnut.

She is equipped for rowing or downwind sailing as well as for an outboard. This shad barge is typical of Goslee's boats, which vary only slightly in length and amount of rocker. Like other Sharptown Barges, she is heavily built and light in draft, capable of carrying a ton of fish.

These boats are no longer used for catching shad with gill nets, as this is currently banned under Maryland law, but are used for other methods of fishing and for general pleasure.

Purchase

84-18-1

John Goslee and Josef Liener at Sharptown, Maryland, in front of a recently built barge, 1989.

Fleming, Richard. "Sharptown Carpenter Continues Old
Tradition of Building Shad Barges." *Sunday Times* (Salisbury) 8
Aug. 1976.

Horton, Tom. "The Shad Barge–Saucy, Graceful and
Disappearing." *Sun* (Baltimore) 4 Jun. 1978.

White, Dan. *Cross Currents in Quiet Water*. Dallas, Texas:
Taylor Publishing Co., 1987.

Plans below are for a Sharptown Barge.

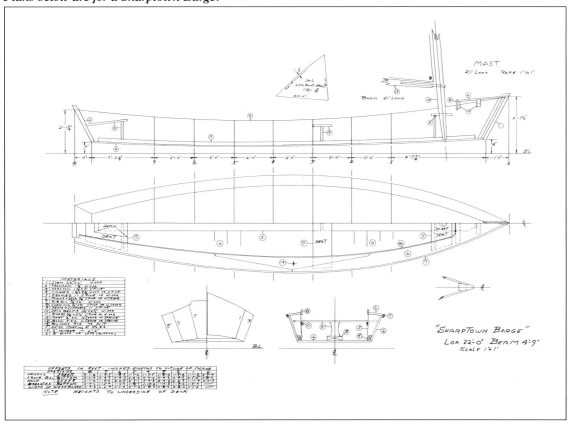

Pound-Net Skiff

Built 1912, Tilghman Island, Maryland,
by John B. Harrison
31' 0" x 8' 2-1/2"

According to Ben Harrison, his father, John B. Harrison, built this boat to serve his 21 pound nets that were set off Poplar Island. It was the first of two such boats built at roughly the same time.

Built of pine and double-ended, the boat's sides have a gentle curve, and there is a slight sheer and some flare fore and aft. The keel, nine inches thick, lies flat for most of its run, rising slightly at the stern. The bottom planks are rabbeted to the keel at the bow and the stern, where there is some deadrise, but the wider bottom planks amidships cross under the keel from chine to chine. The covering board (washboard) and rail on the port side have been replaced more recently than those on the starboard side. The starboard rub rail has worn completely off, and the covering board has worn down to the sheer strake. A 5-1/2-inch-wide bench running down each side was kneeled on when the nets were pulled up. Frames running from the chine to the sheer are of two different sizes and spaced unevenly.

The skiff was usually towed out to the pound-nets and sculled once it reached them; a socket for the sculling oarlock is visible in the stern. The large size of this workboat was necessary to accommodate the large crew necessary to fish the pound nets. The high freeboard was needed because the entire crew would have to work on one side of the boat, heeling it over. Pound-netting was notorious for the rough seas in which it was done, so this boat was particularly heavily built.

Paula Jenkins, the builder's daughter, can recall riding on the boat as it was transported from the Harrison residence, where it was built, to the water for launching. She was three at the time, which dates the boat to 1912.

About 1935, the boat was brought to the

Pound-net skiff, in the early 1940s, at a pound on Maryland's Western Shore. Captain Hedge Fairbanks is third from right; Ben Harrison is on far right.

Western Shore by Ben Harrison, where he and Captain Hedge T. Fairbank used it to tend pound nets. Captain Fairbank eventually became the sole owner of the craft, and the boat remained in his possession until it was donated to the Museum.

Donor: Mrs. Hedge T. Fairbank

70-82-1

"It's Spring–and the Nets Go Out." *Sun* (Baltimore) 19 May 1970.

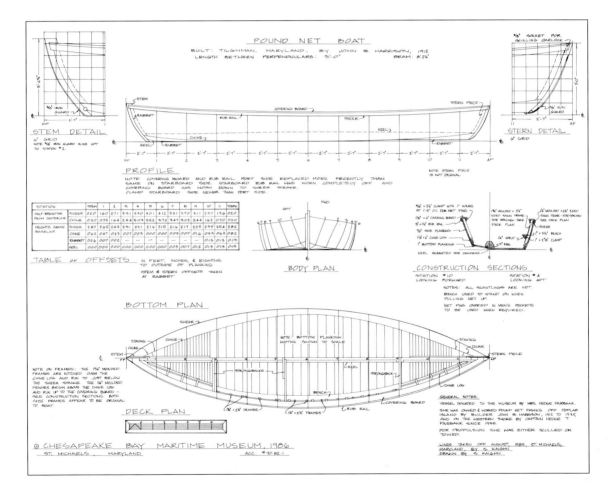

Pram was built as a yacht tender that could travel across ice.

Pram

Built circa 1929-1930, Miles River Neck,
Maryland, by C. Lowndes Johnson
8' 2-1/2" x 3'

In winters before 1930 Lowndes Johnson and his brother, Graham, kept their Q-class yacht, *Vingt Trois*, near Easton in Dixon Cove, North Bend, across the Miles River from their home, "The Harbor". In 1929 their neighbor, Milton Campbell of "The Anchorage", had a small, protected cove dredged at his property. Beginning the next winter, the Johnsons and others moored their yachts in this cove, which they called "Bowes Cove".

To tend these yachts during the winter, Lowndes Johnson built this pram, which he propelled with a push pole. If the pram broke through the ice, Johnson would be secure in this small craft.

The pram is cross-planked and has steel-covered runners under each bilge to allow it to slide across the ice more easily. She is made with one plank on each side and no keelson or chine logs. Two thwarts and a curved stern seat are fitted.

Donor: Robert G. Gavin

77-11-1

Decoy **with C. Lowndes Johnson in the stern.**

Decoy
Pram

Built August–September, 1940, Miles River
Neck, Maryland, by C. Lowndes Johnson
7' 2" x 2' 11-1/2"

Lowndes Johnson built *White Cap II*, a 28-foot cruising ketch, for his own use in 1938. On 15 August 1940, he drew plans for a small pram to be used as a tender with this yacht. He wrote in his diary, "Had to draw it three times before it looked right." He began work on it the following day, and he launched the finished pram on Friday, 13 September 1940. While cruising on *White Cap II*, he kept the pram on deck, just behind the mainmast.

The construction of this pram is unusual. The bottom is formed of three planks, rockered fore-and-aft. There is one plank on each side. The keel plank is no heavier than any of the others, and the garboard strakes form an angle with the keel in addition to the angle formed with the sheer strake, so there are, in essence, two chines.

The bow and stern are decked over, and washboards of five to six inches run down each side.

There is a small rowing seat in the stern for an oarsman facing forward. Sometime before 1950, Johnson placed a second set of rowlock sockets 22 inches aft of the first pair for rowing from this seat. Otherwise, he could row while seated on the foredeck, facing aft.

A year before his death in 1971, Johnson gave this boat to his friend Ernest Tucker.

Donor: Mrs. Ernest Tucker

82-11-1

Widgeon *in St. Michaels harbor.*

Widgeon
Sailing and Rowing Skiff

Built 1949, Miles River Neck, Maryland,
by C. Lowndes Johnson
15' 6" x 4' 2"

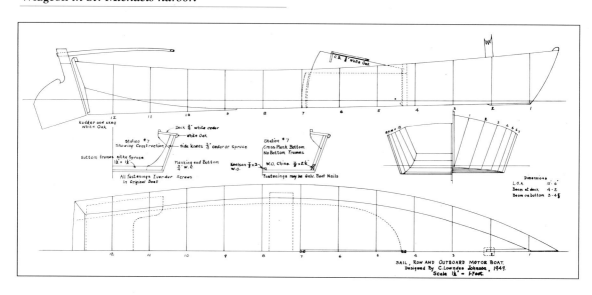

W idgeon is a small sailing skiff built by Lowndes Johnson for his own use. He built the boat to lines he took off an old sailing rowboat he had as a youth. It had been built in 1889 by Quilla Price at Easton Point, Maryland. He and his brother, Graham, added a sailing rig in the 1890s to the Price boat and used it for rowing, sailing, and general utility. It served them well for many years.

According to Josef Liener, a friend of Johnson, *Widgeon* is the only survivor of three or four boats that Lowndes Johnson built from the lines of the old Quilla Price rowboat.

Johnson modified the design slightly when building *Widgeon*, providing a little more deck forward, wider washboards, and a removable hatch

Widgeon *with removable cuddy in place.*

Dilley, Ray. "C. Lowndes Johnson's Widgeon." *Small Boat Journal* 26 (1982).

and cuddy cabin. Instead of the two-stick leg-of-mutton rig, carried by the old boat, *Widgeon* carried a sliding gunter rig, but no jib, on a single raking mast stepped well forward. Later, the rig was altered to a 68-square-foot triangular sail, a cut-down Comet sail, on a taller mast without the yard. *Widgeon* is also fitted for oars and has a sculling notch on the starboard side of the transom.

Widgeon is framed in white oak and planked fore and aft in 3/4-inch white cedar. Bottom frames are 1-1/2-inch square sitka spruce, and the rudder, skeg, and centerboard are 7/8-inch white oak. The date of construction, 1949, is carved into the inside of the transom. There is no deadrise, and the bottom curves up gracefully at the stern. However, the boat generally follows the same construction methods as the Chesapeake flat-bottom workboats, excepting the fore-and-aft planking; there are no complex curves or twists in the planks.

After restoration the skiff was sailed until placed on display in the Small Boat Shed.

Donor: W. Mason Shehan

81-27-1

Pushboat (CBMM 89-8-1) carried on the davits over the stern of the skipjack Stanley Norman.

Pushboat

Built 1937, Dorchester County, Maryland
Attributed to Bronza Parks
11' 11-3/4" x 4' 10"

From the mid-1800s, Maryland and Virginia placed restrictions on oyster dredging under power. Even today, Maryland forbids the use of inboard engines in dredge boats and requires that dredging be done under sail except on Mondays and Tuesdays.

Pushboats were developed to maneuver in and out of harbor and get to and from the oyster "rocks" in a calm. They appeared with the coming of the internal combustion engine and were designed to push the dredgeboat from the stern. When not in use they were carried on davits over the stern of the dredgeboat. No rudder was fitted and they were little more than a large engine. Lines from the davits secured the pushboat to the larger boat.

This pushboat was built in 1937 for use with the two-sail bateau (skipjack) *Stanley Norman*. She may have been built by Bronza Parks of Dorchester County, who built *Stanley Norman*, and was designed with a hard chine and an arc bottom, which was typical of the later pushboats. By the time this one was built, it was common to use converted automobile engines in pushboats, though this one had no engine when she was donated to the Museum.

Donor: Edward Farley

89-8-1

84

GUNNING BOATS

Give me a gun and some old Marsh,
Where the pusher's voice calls mark right!
As the king rail springs from the ditch beyond
then as suddenly drops out of sight. *

George B. Grinnell, writing in *American Duck Shooting* (1901), summarized the Chesapeake Bay in the following statement: "This great body of water, more than 200 miles long, and from four to forty miles width, with its innumerable bays, sounds, broad water and sluggish rivers has unquestionably sheltered more wildfowl than any other body of water in the country, and has been the greatest ducking ground that America has known." Not surprisingly, these prolific gunning grounds brought forth an interesting variety of gunning boats. They form the largest category of small craft at the Museum and can be broken down into five general types: railskiffs (reedbird skiffs), bushwhack boats (sneakboats), sinkboxes, sneakboxes, and sneakskiffs.

The most well-known and successful Chesapeake gunning boat was the sinkbox or "battery." Most accounts credit its origin to New York in the mid-19th century. Shortly after that time it could be found in the Chesapeake, particularly on the Susquehanna Flats in the Upper Bay. Here, miles of wild celery grew, attracting hungry diving ducks, like canvasbacks and redheads, during their winter migration.

Sinkboxes came in several varieties but all resembled a floating coffin more than a boat. A man-sized box open at the top is attached to a platform about six feet wide and ten feet long. Hinged to the edges of this platform are light canvas covered wings which fold out when in use and rise and fall with the waves. The sinkbox is towed to the desired location, anchored, and the craft sunk level with the water by the use of iron wing decoys.

Sinkboxes were first used by market gunners, who were usually watermen or farmers who needed to supplement their income. Towards the end of the 19th century the sinkboxes became popular with "sports" (recreational hunters) from New York, Philadelphia and Baltimore. In order to cater to this demand, sinkbox rigs were created consisting of a "layboat"

or house-boat, one or two skiffs to set out and retrieve the hundreds of decoys required, and a sinkbox. The center for these activities was the town of Havre de Grace where gunning was taken very seriously. About 50 sinkbox rigs were operating around 1920, in the heyday of the sport.

Most of the sinkboxes were of the single body type. Rarer were the double body and sit-down sinkboxes or "tub boxes." The latter provided a marginally more comfortable existence for the hardy gunner.

A variation on the sinkbox was the icebox. The craft had the same coffin shaped compartment and surrounding platform as the sinkbox, but not the hinged canvas wings. Iceboxes were usually equipped with metal runners for hauling over the ice. Once at a spot near open water, a hole was chopped in the ice, and the icebox was inserted so the surrounding platform rested on the ice, supporting the hunter's weight. Decoys were laid out and the accompanying skiff then withdrew beyond range. Icebox and gunner were all in white to aid concealment.

Bushwhacking ducks was another common method of hunting on the Upper Bay. Although the origin of the term is obscure, the method of hunting was fairly simple. A stool of a hundred or so decoys would be set out by two to three gunners in a bushwhack boat (sneakboat). The boat then moved upwind and waited for ducks to decoy. After the ducks alighted, the sneakboat was quietly sculled towards them. When the ducks became alarmed, they flew into the wind, which brought them right over the gunners' sights.

This floating duck blind was unlike any other on the Bay – a cross between a dory and skiff. A sneakboat's dimensions were governed by law: it could not be less than 16 feet long nor less than 20 inches at its lowest point in height.

The craft are marked by high, flaring sides and a flat bottom with several inches of rocker fore and aft. Usually built of cedar, some were cross planked on the bottoms although a frame boat with lengthwise planking was preferred. The boats were painted white to resemble ice floes and were fitted with a canvas screen that extended a

---

* Percy T. Blogg, *There Are No Dull Dark Days*, 1944.

foot or so above the gunwale. The screen provided concealment to the gunner in the bow and the sculler crouching in the stern.

Bushwhack boats started life as tenders to sinkboxes but rapidly became hunting boats in their own right with a license required for their use. When sinkbox rigs were banned by federal law in 1935, bushwhack rigs became the most popular form of duck hunting on the flats. Law required the boats to be rowed or sculled until 1950 when outboard motors were permitted. Many boats were then altered to create a motor well.

Unlike the sneakboat, the sneakbox was not developed locally but had its genesis in New Jersey. This classic hunting boat has many variants but resembles a pumpkin seed in shape, with its spoon-shaped hull and full decks. Hazelton Seaman of West Creek, New Jersey, is credited with the first sneakbox in 1836. The boat can be powered by sail, oar, poling or dragging through the marsh, but the Museum's four examples are all gunning sneakboxes, intended mainly for rowing.

The boats were built for one-man operation, with just enough room below decks for equipment and gunner. A rack abaft the cockpit held the decoys. With brush piled on the deck she became an effective floating blind. A number of sneakboxes found their way to the Upper Bay from New Jersey, although local builders and waterfowlers created their own variations.

Less commonly known than sneakboxes is the diverse group of gunning craft variously known as rail skiffs, push skiffs or reedbird skiffs. "Reedbirding" was a popular form of sport in late summer on the New Jersey and Maryland marshes. The Sora or Carolina rail was preferred game but the Virginia rail and King rail were also sought.

The rail skiffs were flat-bottomed and usually doubled-ended. They were designed for two-man operation with a guide who poled the boat from astern and a gunner forward at the ready. Skiffs were rowed to the marsh, then poled through, working one to two hours either side of high tide when there was water enough to float the boat. A pusher was typically paid $10 for working a tide. As birds were flushed, the guide would cry "mark left" or "mark right" and the "sport" would try his best shot.

The Delaware Ducker was another type of craft that was used for hunting rail in the Chesapeake marshes. Unlike rail skiffs, many of which were built on the Bay, most duckers were imported by out-of-town sportsmen. These double-ended, round-bottomed, lapstrake craft were of a style not familiar to local builders and many were constructed in the boat shops of Philadelphia and surrounding area. Although heavier than a rail skiff, the higher sides of the ducker made it more seaworthy. Many duckers were built for sail although the Museum's examples were designed for rowing and poling.

Probably the most romanticized and fascinating of all gunning boats was the sneakskiff or lighting skiff. The sneakskiff was designed for use with the "big gun," often doubling as a crabbing skiff in summer.

The "big gun" had its origin in the 19th-century English punt gun, a large-bore weapon usually made by a professional gunsmith. The big gun, as usually found on the Chesapeake, was crude, and often home-made from pieces of steel pipe welded together. These guns were primarily used by market gunners up until the Migratory Game Bird Act of 1918. Their use after that date, particularly on the Lower Eastern Shore, branded their owners as "outlaw gunners."

The boat designed for use with the big gun was a doubled-ended skiff whose shape was marked by clear lines and simple construction. The double-ended design was intended to prevent gurgling of dead water at the stern. Sneakskiff was an appropriate description. They were used at night with oars, sculling oar, or paddles, to approach resting ducks quietly. Boat, gun and gunner were usually in white. When close to a flock, paddles would be used to aim the gun horizontally and, by shifting weight, aim could be adjusted vertically. Usually the gunner got only one chance to shoot, as reloading was out of the question in such a small craft.

With the advent of repeating shotguns, the days of the "big gun" were numbered. But the sneakskiff also made an ideal platform for gunners armed with shotguns and a lamp to illuminate the waterfowl. In this mode it was sometimes called a "lighting skiff." By whatever method, the risks were high on the cold and dark winter nights. Accidents were frequent, but the reward could sometimes be a haul of fifty or so ducks.

Over the years the big guns were confiscated and those that were hidden are now curiosities and museum pieces.· They form a fascinating part of the golden era of waterfowling on the Chesapeake from the 1870s to the 1920s.

In addition to the gunning boats at the Chesapeake Bay Maritime Museum, others may be seen at the Upper Bay Museum in Northeast, Maryland, Calvert Marine Museum in Solomons, Maryland, and at the Wildfowl Art Museum in Salisbury, Maryland.

Postcard showing Robert Vandiver in a single-body sinkbox, circa 1907.

Sinkbox (Single-Body)

Date of build unknown, Hooper Island,
Maryland, by Captain John Phillips
10' 2" x 4' 2" (wings closed)

This sinkbox was owned by Captain John Phillips who was a seafood dealer in Cambridge, Maryland, prior to the Second World War.

The sinkbox has a 14-1/2-inch-deep "coffin" that rises like a couch to 11-1/2 inches at the head. This rise was added to alleviate the fatigue brought on by craning the neck to see over the box while lying down. Although the box does not have the protective lead fold up strip usually found at the head, it does have the rectangular fold up strip around the "coffin." This lead strip, when bent upward, provided the sinkbox with a small amount of freeboard, preventing waves from swamping the box.

The head of the box, which was pointed into the wind, has three fold-down, diminishing wings, while the other sides only have one. The diminishing wings, made of canvas stretched over a wood frame, were folded out to help dampen the waves. The wings are fastened by leather hinges, unlike most sinkboxes, which usually have iron barn hinges.

Donor: Dr. Harry M. Walsh
73-54-2

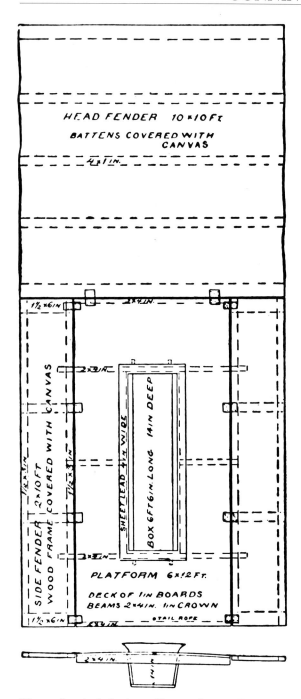

HEAD FENDER 10×10 FT

BATTENS COVERED WITH
CANVAS

4×1 IN.

1½ ×6 IN   2×4 IN.

2×3 IN.

2×10 FT   COVERED WITH CANVAS
WOOD FRAME
SIDE FENDER
7½ ×3 IN.

SHEET LEAD 4½ IN. WIDE
BOX 6 FT 6 IN. LONG   14 IN. DEEP

2×4 IN.

PLATFORM 6×12 FT.

DECK OF 1 IN. BOARDS
BEAMS 2×4 IN.   1 IN. CROWN

1½ ×6 IN   6×4 IN.   TAIL ROPE

2×4 IN.

*Plans of a single body sinkbox in George B.
Grinnell's American Duck Shooting, 1901.*

Sinkbox (Single-Body)

Built circa 1910, Havre de Grace area,
11' 6" x 6' 6" (wings closed)

This sinkbox was used by J. Donald Hawkins of Havre de Grace on the Susquehanna Flats. Hawkins actively gunned for ducks on the Flats up through the 1920s, and was often accompanied by Havre de Grace decoy carver, Bob McGaw. David J. Smith, grandson of Donald Hawkins, remembers his grandfather loading the sinkbox into the back of a Model T Ford truck and taking it to the gunning grounds. According to the donor, the sinkbox may have been built for Hawkins by Bob McGaw.

The box itself has 15-inch-deep sides that are built with some flare. The width of the "coffin" at the head is 19 inches filling out to 23 inches amidships and finishing at 12 inches at the foot. The platform has the V-shaped and rectangular sheet-lead weather edges that gave the box a few inches of freeboard when bent up.

The windward diminishing wings are of solid wood while the side wings are of wood covered with canvas. The wings are attached by metal barn door hinges. This sinkbox has 12 color silhouettes of canvasback ducks painted on the windward wings and platform. Whether these painted ducks helped to camouflage the box is debatable, but they are a rare feature.

This sinkbox was restored by the donor in 1946, and used by him to make a color documentary film about sinkbox gunning.

Donor: David J. Smith
75-30-1

Sinkbox (Double-Body)

Date and place of build unknown
12' 3-1/2" x 7' 1" (wings closed)

The double-bodied or side-by-side sinkbox is a rare variation of this gunning craft. The exact place of origin for the double sinkbox type is obscure, although accounts date their existence on the Bay as far back as 1889. Double-bodied as well as single sinkboxes were built by rack of eye by decoy carvers, guides and backyard builders. Plans, too, were available. George B. Grinnell's *American Duck Shooting* (1901) contains drawings and dimensions of a single and double sinkbox.

Double-bodied sinkboxes could increase the number of birds downed at one time by permitting two gunners to work together. Many sportsmen friends enjoyed sharing the moment of the hunt together in a double box. Prior to this, two single sinkboxes would be rafted near each other to produce the same effect.

The hunting guides saw the double box as a mixed blessing. The guides could take on twice as many "sports" for a day using a double, increasing their profits. But the double box was hard to handle, heavy and awkward, and could be nearly unmanageable to lay out in choppy water. The weight required to sink a double rig to water level was considerable and numerous flat iron decoys, weighing up to 25 pounds apiece, were employed.

Donor: S. Hallock duPont

67-67-1

Sinkbox and bushwhack boat.

Sinkbox (Sit-Down Model)

Date and place of build unknown
12' 8-1/2" x 6' 2" (wings closed)

The sit-down sinkbox or "tub box" is by far the rarest sinkbox type. It was developed in the Carolinas, probably in the Currituck Sound area in the early 1900s, then spread to the Chesapeake. The box took a great deal of weight to "take her down" and was difficult to manage while laying out. The sit-down models also took more time and materials to build.

These models were never widespread on the Upper Bay, although they did improve comfort. Sinkbox shooting is a cold and wet way to hunt; the sit-down model made it tolerable. A "sport" could spend more time out on the water by placing a lantern between his legs and covering himself with blankets, making the sit-down box as comfortable as a blind.

Donor: Dr. Harry M. Walsh

75-26-1

Icebox

Date and place of build unknown
7' 10" x 4' 10"

The icebox was used the same way as a sinkbox, but was meant for use on ice. Duck hunters often had an icebox built just in case their hunting area froze over. This icebox was used by J. Donald Hawkins of Havre de Grace who hunted at the Susquehanna Flats up through the 1920s.

This box has the same type of coffin shape found on Hawkins's sinkbox (CBMM 75-30-1). The sides are 13-3/8 inches deep with some flare. The box measures 18-1/4 inches in width at the head, growing to 19 inches amidships and finishing 10-3/4 inches at the foot. The box has fold-out floorboards that are cut to fit. Floorboards kept the gunner out of the bilge and were standard equipment on sinkboxes and iceboxes alike. The icebox has stubby wings on which the box rested while inserted in the ice hole, keeping the box from slipping through. These wings are supported by oak cross frames and are reinforced by two sets of top nailers. The bottom of the box has two oak ice runners fitted with steel half rounds for moving over the ice. This icebox was served by a sneakbox that is also in the Museum's collection (CBMM 75-30-3).

Donor: David J. Smith

75-30-2

Icebox

Built circa 1925, Harford County, Maryland, by Will Hopkins
7' 5" x 3' 9"

This icebox was made for Dr. Samuel W. Reeves II, an army doctor stationed at the Aberdeen Proving Grounds. It is built of pine and is trapezoidal in shape. The box measures 25-1/2 inches at the head and 15 inches at the foot and the plumb sides are 11 inches deep. Wings are made from two 6-inch-wide boards mounted to oak cross frames. The cross frames are fastened by wing nuts, which allow the wings to be removed for storage and transport. The wings also follow the trapezoidal shape. Fitted to the bottom are two oak ice runners faced with steel half rounds.

The icebox was towed over the ice by a tender, in this case a sneakbox (CBMM 74-31-1), to a spot near an opening in the ice where ducks might alight to feed. A hole was cut in the ice to the shape of the box, which was then inserted. The tender would then lay out the decoy stool and retire to a safe distance. The gunner would either be dressed in white or cover himself with a white blanket.

When the Bay froze, an icebox hunter's chances were better than those of sinkbox gunners who had to depend on finding open water for their rigs.

Donor: Samuel W. Reeves III

74-31-2

Icebox used by J. Donald Hawkins of Havre de Grace, Maryland.

PC
Motorized Sinkbox Tender

Built circa 1928, Horner's Point, Maryland,
by Emory Howlett
20' x 5' 5"

Motorized sinkbox tender PC *on exhibit at* **CBMM, 1992.**

The motorized tender *Pisscutter* or *PC* is a unique member of the Museum's collection of hunting craft. The boat was built for J. Smith Michael. Like the oar-powered bushwhack boats, it was used to lay out decoys and retrieve downed ducks. The propeller is recessed in a tunnel built into the after portion of the flat bottom. This tunnel stern enabled *PC* to operate in shoal water. At some point the craft's bottom, engine cover, and forward bulkhead were replaced with plywood and the hull fiberglassed. These repairs most likely took place in the 1960s.

The boat is equipped with a pre-1927 four-cylinder Continental car engine. The boat's scantlings show a history of repair and replacement, and it is difficult to distinguish original construction from later additions; her tunnel stern may have been incorporated later. *PC* has a raked stem, moderately flaring sides, and considerable rocker.

Donor: Joseph Louch

79-38-1

Bushwhack Boat (Sneakboat)

Built 1923, Havre de Grace, Maryland,
by James T. Holly
17' 5" x 5' 1-1/4"

James T. Holly (1855-1935), an expert decoy carver and bushwhack boat builder, lived in the Havre de Grace area. He is credited with the bushwhack boat design, which he developed by modifying a type of fishing boat used on the Susquehanna Flats. The ability to handle rough water while loaded with a sinkbox or 300 decoys made the use of bushwack boats by duck hunters widespread. Later they were used as gunning boats in their own right.

Holly built this boat with white pine for the sides, oak for the transom, and chestnut for the knees. The boat has three strakes per side set with heavy flare. This great flare gave the boat a heavy carrying capacity. There are seven sawn frames and the bottom is fore-and-aft planked and set with a substantial amount of rocker.

A one-piece dory-like stem is notched at the sheer line to accept the rubrail, giving the rail a finished appearance. The boat's breast hook is 15 inches long on the sheer line and is a substantial part of the boat's structure. The transom, which is set at a 40 degree rake from the perpendicular, is four feet wide at the sheer line. Her inwale is mounted right to the plank, giving the boat closed gunwales. Three walking boards are inside: the center board runs the whole length of the boat, while its flank boards cover the four frames under the two rowing seats. There are two foot braces on the center walking board 27 inches abaft each seat. Two sets of oars and a 10-foot sculling oar complete her outfit.

Donor: H. Rodney Sharp

68-52-1

Henderson, Carl. "The 'Holly Boat.'" *Havre de Grace Decoy Festival.* Havre de Grace, Md: Havre de Grace Decoy Festival Committee, 1984.

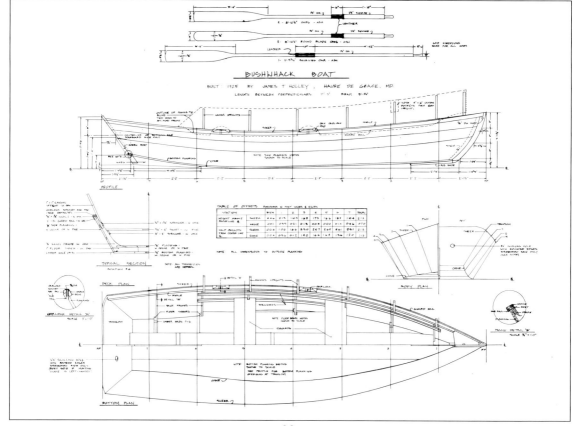

Bushwhack Boat

Built mid 1920s, Havre de Grace, Maryland,
by Paul Gibson
16' 5" x 5'

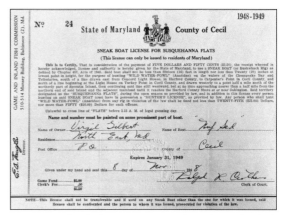

This craft is cruder in construction than its Holly-built counterpart and was built by noted decoy carver, Paul Gibson (1902-1985). She has a two-piece stem, with the false stem secured by heavy bolts. The stem is joined by a 1-3/4-inch thick, unfinished, triangular breast hook. Cross planking of 6-inch boards is supported by 3-inch chine logs and a 10-inch-wide keelson plank. The boat has two strakes per side with the heavy flare characteristic of the type. Six sets of side frames of 3/4-inch stock taper to the inwale. The inwales and the rub rails are of 1-3/4-inch stock and appear heavy on the boat. The bushwhacker's canvas blind or "dodger" is 10-1/2 inches high and is supported by six staves. These staves are wedged between the inwale and a light batten that does not appear to be original to the boat's construction.

Unlike the Holly-built boat, this sneakboat has a motor well cut out of the transom. Maryland law prohibited the use of motors in sneakboats until 1950. The motor well, a later alteration, is simply a rectangular hole set in 10 inches from the left side on the transom, and boxed in. The outboard was only to be used when traveling to or from the hunting spot or picking up downed birds and cripples.

In accordance with Maryland boating and game laws the bushwhack licence number and owner's name had to be displayed on a prominent part of the boat. The number 233 and the donor's name, Gary Pensell, appear on the inside of the transom in black letters.

Donor: Gary Pensell

66-20-1

Holly bushwhack boat (CBMM 68-52-1) on display, 1984.

Atropos
Barnegat Bay Sneakbox

Built 1947, Spray Beach, New Jersey,
by William Cranmer
12' 1-1/2" x 4' 1"

This sneakbox was built for James C. Hornor, a professional sportsman, who represented the DuPont Powder Manufacturing Corporation at sportsman's gatherings, shoots, and hunting expeditions. Hornor had her built by sneakbox builder William Cranmer of Spray Beach, New Jersey. The boat was used by Hornor while duck hunting up and down the eastern seaboard, and his travels often brought him to the Chesapeake Bay area.

The boat is built with traditional sneakbox details and construction techniques. The one difference is that the boat was covered, hull and decks, with fiberglass, allowing her to be dry-sailed. She is equipped with two push poles: one used for poling over the marsh, the other a hook for pulling the boat over the ice. Traditional stool boards are attached at the stern to create a box on the deck in which decoys could be stored while underway. The boat, although not a sailing model, has a dagger board slot. This slot was built into gunning models to accommodate a 58-1/2-inch dagger board called a spud board. This was jammed down into the mud to anchor the boat in place. It was also allowed to drag along the bottom while setting out and picking up decoys. Inside the cockpit the boat has a single gun rack and a small shelf for shotgun shell boxes. The cockpit is fitted with contoured walking boards, and there is a canoe-like back rest that can be placed between these boards and the cockpit coaming.

The boat has folding oarlocks of oak which are notched with a small triangle on the bottom for drainage. There is a toprail, referred to as an ice rail on a sneakbox, that held ice and snow, as well as mud and reeds for camouflage. The cockpit is covered with two hatches that overlap on the seam. A small pole hooked under the fore hatch was used to support the canvas spray dodger on deck.

The name *Atropos* comes from the mythological Fate that cuts the thread of life.

Donor: James C. Hornor

84-11-1

Cranmer-built 1947 Sneakbox, 1991.

Sneakbox (CBMM 75-30-3) used by J. Donald Hawkins on the Susquehanna Flats.

Sneakbox

Date unknown, built in Havre de Grace area, Maryland
11' 4" x 3' 6"

The sneakbox that Hazelton Seaman of West Creek, New Jersey, first built in 1836 spawned many variations in different parts of the country. This interesting model was built in the Havre de Grace area and was used by J. Donald Hawkins who hunted at the Susquehanna Flats through the 1920s. Hawkins used this sneakbox in conjunction with his sinkbox and icebox rigs, which were also donated to the Museum (CBMM 75-30-1, 75-30-2). Hawkins was often accompanied on hunting trips by his close friend Bob McGaw, famed Havre de Grace area decoy carver.

This craft departs from traditional sneakbox construction with the addition of a side strake and plumb stem. Sneakbox variants with side strakes were in existence by the 1890s. The boat has a kayak-like hull shape and oval cockpit opening.

The boat resembles a variation of the Great South Bay Ice Scooter discussed in an article written by H. Percy Ashley in the November 1904 issue of *The Rudder* magazine. He stated that the scooter is an all season boat which would perform well as a duck boat. The main difference between the two boats is that the scooter has a rounded stern and the Museum's example has a transom stern. The scooter may have been the builder's inspiration for a craft that could move over the ice to tend an icebox.

Each side has a single strake of 4-inch width that tapers to 3 inches at the transom, without flare. The plumb stem appears to be of one piece and is 4 inches at the profile. Bottom planking is fore and aft and the side strakes and bottom seams are covered with copper sheathing for protection against ice. The boat has a combination of sawn and steamed frames and a solid bulkhead two feet from the bow. A top ice rail was used to secure ice and snow for camouflage. Her oval cockpit has a coaming that was steamed into place and spliced on either side. The white craft has runners of oak with half-round metal strips to help in crossing the ice.

Donor: David J. Smith
75-30-3

Sneakbox

Date and place of build unknown
10' 2" x 4' 2"

T his is an arc-bottom composite type as described in Peter Guthorn's *The Sea Bright Skiff and Other Jersey Shore Boats*, differing from the traditional Jersey sneakbox by having a side strake and a deeper hull. This type appeared in the late 1890s, offering much more carrying capacity than a traditional sneakbox design.

The box has a 5-inch wide strake that tapers to 4 inches at the transom and 2 inches at the bow. Her 29- by 47-inch cockpit appears proportionally large for the boat. The cockpit is outfitted with a coaming that is reinforced at the corners by knees. Mounted inside the coaming on the fore-and-aft sections are two battens that support an undersized cockpit hatch made of plywood. The hatch is too small on the sides to be effective and is probably not original to the boat. An outside rail (or grass rail) on either side of the cockpit allowed the hunter to secure grass and other camouflage material to the boat to create a blind. A hand scythe was considered standard equipment on a sneakbox for cutting camouflage material in the marsh.

Two ice runners of 1-1/2-inch oak are bent to the heavy rocker of the hull bottom. At some time the craft was covered with fiberglass that is now beginning to separate from the wooden hull.

Donors: Mr. and Mrs. E. Cornman

73-25-1

Sneakbox

Built 1925, Harford County, Maryland,
by Will Hopkins
12' x 4'

T his sneakbox was built by Will Hopkins for Samuel W. Reeves II who was an army doctor stationed at Aberdeen Proving Ground. Will Hopkins had a large farm on Swan Creek where Reeves often gunned.

The boat has a flat sheer line and less rocker than the sneakboxes built in the New Jersey area where pronounced sheer and rocker were added after the 1880s. This trend did not seem to carry over into the Upper Bay-built sneakboxes. The boat has a mixture of sneakbox and scooter influences in its design.

She is built of white cedar that was brought from Wading River, New Jersey. The oak frames and knees are from the Will Hopkins farm. Her bottom is protected by sheathing and two ice runners. The hull is made of nine planks supported by 12 steamed and three sawn frames. Unlike most sneakboxes, she departs from traditional methods by the omission of the harpin member. The boat does not have much of the rocker or amidships arch that is common on most sneakboxes, making the harpin unnecessary.

This example, and the "scooter-like" sneakbox (CBMM 75-30-3) in the collection, were used as icebox tenders. The gunners, usually two in number, poled or pulled the sneakbox over the ice with the icebox filled with decoys in tow. The gunners would head for a natural opening in the ice where the tide broke through and chop a hole a few yards distant from the opening for the icebox. Once the icebox and one of the gunners were in place, the decoys were transferred to the sneakbox, from which the other gunner laid them out in the water. The gunner's companion then moved the sneakbox to a distance and waited to recover downed birds.

Donor: Samuel W. Reeves III

74-31-1

Sneakbox built by Will Hopkins.

Delaware Ducker

Date and place of build unknown
15' 1-1/4" x 3' 9"

The Delaware ducker may be the earliest type of reedbird gunning boat. Peter Guthorn, author of *The Sea Bright Skiff and Other Jersey Shore Boats*, has traced ducker builders as far back as the 1850s. The boat's popularity, however, did not reach a noticeable point until the 1880s. This ducker, as well as the other two in the Museum's collection, was built for rowing and not for sail.

The name A. M. Beitler is stamped twice underneath the walking boards, and once on the inside of the keel. Abraham Merklee Beitler (1853-1935) was a judge of Common Pleas in Philadelphia at the turn of the century. The ducker that he had built is a beautiful example, although the builder's name is unknown. Judge Beitler was fond of reedbird shooting and his family had a house at Plum Point near Annapolis.

Gunners from the Philadelphia area often brought duckers from that area to the Upper Bay for hunting in the marshes.

This ducker exhibits the fine detail that was traditionally given this type of craft. The sheer strake, seat, and platform supports, as well as the walking boards, are finished with a beaded edge. The rub strip is also tapered at bow and stern, a classic ducker detail. The pusher's deck is fitted nicely and adds to the boat's shapely appearance. The aft deck thwart is cut to a gentle heart shape, suggesting that this boat was meant for more than gunning rail birds. The stem of the boat rises a bit above the gunwale line and was once finished in a stem cap, another traditional detail. The cap has been worn down, a victim of long use. Another interesting detail is the 20 hooks mounted under the gunwale. These hooks once supported a canvas sheet that was laid into the cockpit. This inlaid sheet was used while gunning to keep debris out of the bilge, making it easy to keep the boat's interior clean. It was also handy for keeping a lady's dress out of the bilge while she was out rowing.

Delaware Ducker built for A. M. Beitler, seen here in 1991.

"Sports" were generally rowed to the hunting area and then poled through the marshes. At one time this boat was fitted with two sets of rowlocks, but only the set amidships remains.

She is a lapstrake boat with seven strakes on each side on 17 steam-bent frames. An interesting construction detail is the protective ice runners built into the keel. The two garboard strakes do not sit flush with the keel, but hang over, giving the appearance of a sunken keel. The space is filled with two triangular pieces of wood that are fitted to the stem and stern post and mounted on the keel. Two runners of square stock are affixed to the keel tight against the two garboards, making a trough. This assembly protected the keel and added strength.

This boat has many traditional Delaware ducker details and is a good example of the thought and skill that was built into these craft.

Donor unknown

66-199-1

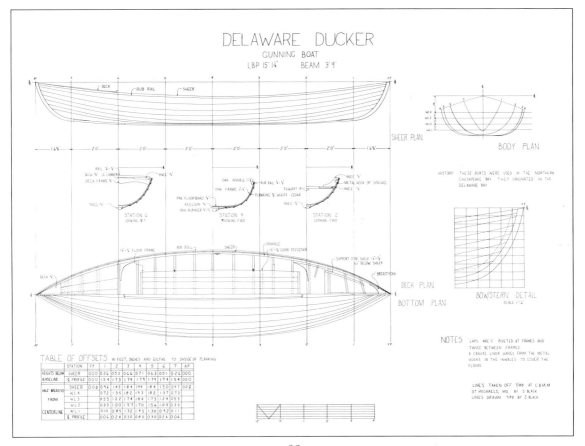

Delaware Ducker

Date unknown, built in Darby, Pennsylvania,
by Keystone Boat Works
15' 4" x 4' 2"

Ducker built by Keystone Boat Works as it appeared in 1990.

B uilt by the Keystone Boat Works as hull number 1052, this ducker represents a production, rather than a "dressed", model. This demonstrates that additional details were simply not needed or cost effective for the sportsman's market. The boat's poling platform aft is covered with rubber matting, and has an edge strip on all sides. The poler placed his foot against this edge strip while pushing, helping him steer. The boat also has two sets of oarlocks on block risers on the gunwales.

The ducker has one standard fixed seat forward. Generally, other rowing seats were movable box seats that were contoured to the walking boards, and could be stowed. This kept the cockpit open, allowing the poler to trim the boat over the marshes.

This example has the customary seven strakes per side on 15 steam-bent frames. The boat is fastened with copper rivets throughout. The stem and stern posts rise above the sheer line and are capped by a brass rub strip which runs down stem and stern and splits to form two ice runners on the outside of the keel. This model has less of a slack bilge than the other two duckers in the collection, providing greater initial stability for standing while gunning and poling.

Donor: C. Douglas Buck, Jr.

78-24-1

Delaware Ducker

Built circa 1920, New Jersey
15' 3" x 4' 1"

T he New Jersey side of the Delaware River had a number of builders who produced duckers. The Museum has one New Jersey-built example, which differs slightly from the two that are attributed to the Philadelphia school. The poling platform is mounted below deck level on two battens, rather than at gunwale level. The uncapped stem and stern posts are joined by two small breast hooks at the gunwale line. Dressed edges on the boat, or any other type of adornment, are absent.

This example has two thwart seats of 1-1/2-inch stock mounted on thin battens. The workmanship on them, as well as on the walking boards, is not consistent with the rest of the boat, suggesting that they are later additions. There is one set of rowlocks amidships. A metal hook mounted near the starboard thwart forward secured the push-pole while rowing.

While this ducker's interior shows a history of modification, the boat's overall appearance is typical of the type. Interiors vary according to purpose and model, usually with traditional arrangements that date to the 1850s.

Donor: J. Avery Draper

86-43-1

Old Garvey Box with its hatch pulled back.

Gunning Garvey Box

Built circa 1929, probably in New Jersey
10' x 3' 9"

The New Jersey garvey was one of the most well-known scow types in America. Of the garveys, the gunning garvey was the smallest type built. She was a simple craft to build compared with a sneakbox and could perform the same type of service for the hunter.

The Museum's example has 7-3/4-inch-wide side strakes that are set plumb, but at a slight curve. The sides join a straight transom and a flat, raked bow. The box has a cross-planked flat bottom, which has an equal amount of rise or rocker at bow and stern. A stern post of oak and a small skeg are fitted to the stern.

The garvey does not have chine logs, but relies on the side planks to support the bottom. The keelson stops when the bottom starts its rise, and two knees are notched into the keelson to serve as unbeveled stem and stern posts.

Her deck is set with substantial camber, measuring three inches from the sheer line. A rectangular cockpit opening is covered by a one-piece hatch. Unlike a two-piece hatch which could be taken along and provided partial shelter, a one-piece hatch had to be removed entirely.

In place is the original set of cedar stool boards, which kept the decoys from sliding off the arched deck when the garvey was underway. The boat's folding oarlocks of oak are supported by a prop when in use, which is wedged between the oarlock and the deck.

Evidence that this garvey may once have been a sailing model consists of a hole 10 inches forward of the cockpit which may have been a mast partner, and filled screw holes where a forestay and shrouds may have been located. The absence of a mast step confuses the issue.

Donor: Mrs. A.M. Parry

79-39-1

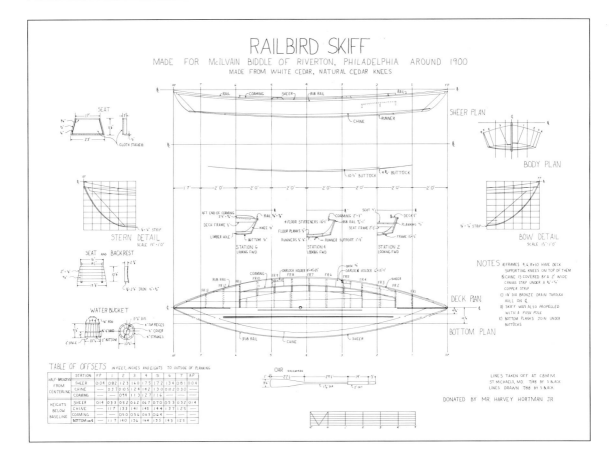

Rail Skiff

Built circa 1900, Philadelphia area,
builder unknown
15' 7" x 3' 3-1/4"

The rail skiffs of the turn-of-the-century were built for the specialized purpose of hunting the marshes for reedbirds. The Chesapeake Bay marshes were enthusiastically gunned by many gentlemen from all over the east coast.

This rail skiff, a product of a professional builder, was made for H. McIlvain Biddle of Riverton, near Philadelphia, and is a beautiful example of the type.

The skiff has one 10-inch-wide cedar strake per side, set with substantial flare. The type is often referred to as a plank boat because of its single strake construction. The bottom is planked fore and aft with five boards. She has a great degree of rocker, which combined with the flare made a boat that could handle choppy water. A sharp bow and stern enabled the boat to knife through the reeds.

The stem and stern posts have a brass rub strip

that finishes at a small skeg. The bottom has two oak runners with brass rub strips mounted about five inches in from her chine. The skiff's chine seams are covered with a strip of canvas, protected by a metal strip screwed over the canvas on the seam. This sealed the seam and eliminated leaks from the swelling and shrinking of the wood. This was important as the boats were only used for shooting a few months each year, and were laid up in the off-season.

The skiff has small end decks that are supported by two thwarts underneath, joined by washboards and finished with a cockpit coaming. The stern deck is larger than the fore, and provides the pusher with a platform. The "sport", who also stands while gunning, is provided with a platform that is set below the deck line, behind the fore deck. There are two movable seats: one of contoured slats, the other a trapezoidal frame

Biddle rail skiff, with original water bucket, 1991.

covered with canvas. These could be moved to suit the rower's own form, and stowed while poling. Thirteen sawn frames of white cedar are joined with natural cedar knees.

Two sets of oarlocks are fitted. The after set is inlaid into a raised block that has a heavy bevel. The forward position is fitted with a set of twist lock rowlocks that appear to be later additions.

Donor: Harvey Hortman, Jr.

84-21-1

Rail Skiff

Built 1923, Elkton, Maryland,
by Samuel Hopkins
14' 11" x 3' 5"

This craft represents a type that was influenced by rail skiffs brought down by hunters from the Delaware River area. These boats were built by local builders or guides for the hunting trade. Therefore, one may find a variety of design modifications and qualities in the railbird skiffs built for use in the Chesapeake. This type has been referred to as an Elk River craft because of her shallow draft.

She has only slight flare and slight rocker, suggesting that the builder did not intend the boat for rough water use. The "sport's" platform is set about three inches below the gunwale line on three thwarts. The pusher's platform, which is set in the stern on three thwarts, is positioned right under the gunwale. This height increased the guide's overall scanning view.

The boat has a single 11-inch strake on each side, fastened to 13 sawn frames, and the bottom is made of three wide boards. The stem and stern posts are of two-piece construction, which eliminates the need to cut a stem rabbet. A rub strip runs about a quarter of the length of the boat under bow and stern, but there are no half round brass rub strips or oak runners that are usually present on the bottom of rail skiffs. Two sets of oarlocks are mounted.

This skiff came with a push pole, a gun rack, and a retrieving net to scoop up the downed birds. She is also equipped with a rowing seat, which is decorated with a bead and is set on two substantial wooden arches.

Donor: Edward H. Duffy

69-97-1

Rail skiff built by Samuel Hopkins in 1923.

Rail Skiff

Date unknown, built in the Patuxent River area
16' 2" x 3' 6"

This rail skiff was locally built, possibly by a guide for the sportsman trade. It was not uncommon for a guide to build his own boat to save on costs. This unknown builder produced a simple but sturdy boat that met his needs. She is the only square-stern rail skiff in the collection. It resembles three skiffs photographed on the Patuxent River by Brooke Meanley and included in his book, *Birds and Marshes of the Chesapeake Bay*. Before Patuxent River builders produced the square-sterned skiffs in the early 20th century, they mainly turned out the traditional double-ended version.

Many sportsmen came to the Patuxent in late summer or early fall to shoot rail. A delightful account is given by Percy T. Blogg in *There Are No Dull Dark Days*.

The square stern, which is 18-1/2 inches at the sheer line, gave the pusher more stability and added to the buoyancy of the skiff. Local builders were familiar with rail skiffs that were brought to the Bay by outside sportsmen, and often incorporated some construction details found on these boats in their own building techniques. This skiff demonstrates this combination, with details such as a tapered rub rail at the bow and a substantial flare. The skiff's cross planking set on 3-inch by 3/4-inch chine logs suggests its local construction. The skiff has three thwarts, two of which are seats; the forward thwart is notched twice so the push-pole can lie secure. The stern seat is set 20 inches forward of the transom, giving room for a removable pusher's platform set on two battens.

This boat is an excellent example of a skiff type built on the Bay for a specific purpose and demonstrates how area builders incorporated outside details to suit their own tastes.

Donor: John McKenny

66-2-1

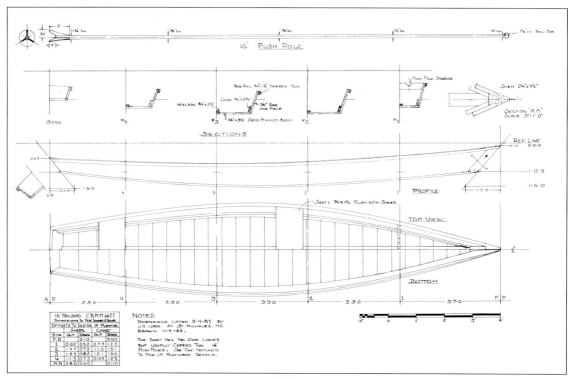

Eugene Townsend, probably on the Cohansey River, circa 1935. The rail skiff was built for Townsend, circa 1895.

Rail Skiff

Built circa 1895, place of build unknown
15' x 3' 9"

This skiff was built for Eugene Townsend of Philadelphia who, at the turn-of-the-century, was president of the Sora Club in Bridgeton, New Jersey. The Sora Club, which was located on the Cohansey River, was an elite hunting club for reedbird hunting enthusiasts.

These high-quality skiffs often found their way out of the clubs and into the Chesapeake for hunting excursions, where their design details were frequently copied by local builders.

The skiff was professionally built and has some noteworthy details. The boat has very little flare or rocker, but the bottom is set with a slight athwartships arch. The skiff is fore-and-aft planked on the bottom with three boards that are rounded to meet the side strake. Stem and stern profiles are quarter circles and cut proud at the sheer into a finished cap. The skiff's 12 sawn frames are very slender and add grace to the boat. Her decks have a noticeable camber and are cut with three scuppers on each side for drainage. The cockpit coaming is heavier fore and aft than on the sides so the pusher can place his feet against it while poling. Paint is a two-tone scheme of dead grass yellow and muted blue. These colors were popular with reedbirders who did not need to worry about camouflage like the duck hunters.

The boat came with a triangular box with flared sides that fits securely under the bow or stern deck. This box was used to store gunning supplies and was set up on the deck while hunting to make its contents accessible. It also is painted in the two-tone scheme of the skiff.

Donor: Henry Pease

79-2-1

Summer Duck *in 1990.*

Summer Duck *circa 1909, with Otto Eisenlohr of Philadelphia in the bow. Poling is Captain Joseph Heisler of Charlestown, Maryland.*

Summer Duck
Rail Skiff

Built circa 1900, place unknown
15' 6" x 3' 9"

S ummer Duck is the only named rail skiff in the collection. She was owned by Otto Eisenlohr of Philadelphia who headed the successful Eisenlohr and Bros. Cigar Manufacturing Company. Eisenlohr often came to the Chesapeake in the autumn to take advantage of the fine gunning sport. He was frequently accompanied by Captain Joseph Heisler of Charlestown who acted as guide and poler. Captain Heisler was a commercial fisherman and market hunter, who, according to his grandson, Nelson H. McCall, did not normally hire out to sportsmen. McCall feels that his grandfather saw the Eisenlohrs as more than "sports" and as colorful people with whom he enjoyed spending time.

The skiff's 14-inch sides are each made of two strakes of white pine. The bottom, which is fore-and-aft planked, has a fair amount of rocker, but does not have any athwartships arch. The skiff's eight sawn frames are of good size and join with 16 natural-crook sassafras knees, giving the boat a great deal of strength. The craft's stem and stern posts finish in the traditional cap, and these posts appear to be one piece. The skiff has two breast hooks which join a substantial inwale laid directly onto the sides, creating closed gunwales. Although there are no washboards or decks, the pusher is provided with a platform that is mounted in the stern below the sheer line. This platform, like the smaller one forward, is mounted on two thwarts and is set level with the waterline. The boat was originally fitted with one set of rowlocks amidships, the second set being added by McCall.

The boat came equipped with a crow's foot push-pole, oars, and a net with a bamboo shaft that was used to retrieve the downed birds.

Donor: Nelson H. McCall

78-14-1

Gunning Skiff

Built 1947, Crocheron, Maryland, by John Elliot
15' 4-1/2" x 4' 1"

This dory stern skiff was built by John Elliot of Crocheron, Maryland, who was a market hunter and boatbuilder. He is credited with building over 100 boats of different types before his death in 1968 at the age of 75.

The skiff was built for a Mr. Meyers of Delaware who used it for duck hunting in the Tedious Bay area. This was one of two skiffs built for Meyers, who ordered a double-ender and a skiff with a transom for an outboard motor. The overall appearance is similar to that of a Sharptown Barge (CBMM 84-18-1), but it is much shorter in length than that type.

The skiff is of lapstrake construction having two strakes on each side with only minimal flare. A 1-by 5-inch keel log is fastened through the bottom with common nails that are clinched back into the bottom boards. The boat has four sets of side frames or side cleats, washboards that run back to the transom, and a foredeck.

Although the boat resembles a market gunner's sneakskiff, it was used only for sport hunting. The fact that the builder was a former market gunner may be responsible for the boat's similarity to earlier big-gun sneakskiffs.

Donor: Ralph V. Mills

74-18-1

John Elliot, skiff builder and hunter, at his home in Crocheron, Maryland.

Sneakskiff displayed with a punt gun at the Chesapeake Bay Maritime Museum.

Sneakskiff

Date and place of build unknown
16' 4" x 3' 5"

This sneakskiff (pictured at left) is a good example of the type that Howard I. Chapelle states, in *Chesapeake Bay Crabbing Skiffs*, developed from double-ended crabbing skiffs around the turn of the century. The sneakskiff, as a type, resembles the double-ended Smith Island crabbing skiffs in construction and design. The main differences between them are the shorter length, slimmer beam, and lack of rocker in the sneakskiff. The beam of the vessel was determined by the comfortable width of a gunner's arms in the position he would use while propelling his skiff with hand paddles when close to feeding ducks.

The skiff has one 12-inch strake per side and the bottom is flat and cross planked. The 10 sets of side frames are notched to fit over the chine log and the inwale is set on top of the frames, creating closed gunwales. She has a 2-inch-wide keelson for longitudinal support. The craft is partially decked with the foredeck supporting the muzzle portion of the "big gun". On the thwart is a movable chock for the butt of the gun which allows it a limited traverse.

Donor: Dr. Harry M. Walsh

73-54-1

Sneakskiff (Lighting Skiff)

Built circa 1930, Fishing Creek, Dorchester County, Maryland, by Milford S. (Eagle) Creighton
14' 7" x 3' 9"

The lighting skiff was built by famed market hunter "Eagle" Creighton (1888-1986) of Fishing Creek. Creighton was born on Barren Island, across Tar Bay from Fishing Creek, and supported himself as a commercial and sport fisherman as well as a market hunter and boat-builder. He worked for area boatbuilder Humes Wallace and was also employed at the Oxford Boatyard.

This type of sneakskiff is referred to as a lighting skiff, because it was used with a large lamp (jacklight) set on the bow for use with an automatic shotgun rather than a "big gun." Eagle Creighton is credited in Harry M. Walsh's book, *The OutLaw Gunner*, with being the first to introduce the Remington Model 11 automatic shotgun in his area, which he used to shoot twice the number of ducks as he could with a "big gun" in the same amount of time. At night the gunner did not need to worry about the silhouette of his skiff and could give the boat more freeboard. The thwart seat, used as a butt support for the "big gun", was no longer needed. This increased the operating capacity of the skiff, and now two gunners shooting new automatic shotguns from either side of the blinding light could down more ducks.

The craft is built with one 14-inch strake on each side. Five sets of frames or side cleats brace the side planks and support the washboards, and are notched to fit over the chine logs. Her bottom is cross planked and flat; a keelson and heavy chine logs are fitted.

When not used for gunning, these skiffs were often used for dipnet crabbing in shoal water, the handle of the dipnet often serving as a push pole. A toe rail helps the poler keep directional control. A pair of oarlocks is mounted, and the oars were probably pushed while standing up, rather than pulled in the conventional manner.

Donor: Dr. Harry M. Walsh

75-24-1

ONE-DESIGN BOATS

As yacht racing increased in popularity through the last half of the 19th century, racing vessels increased in size, sophistication, and expense. Catering to wealthy yacht owners, yacht designers attempted to out-build the boats of their competitors. In response to complaints of the escalating costs, one-design racing classes appeared in which hull specifications, rig, and yacht equipment could be standardized in the interests of ensuring fair competition.

One-design classes had several distinct advantages over open classes. Their use, for example, promoted competition among captains and crews, instead of owners and designers. Open classes were becoming too expensive for most yachtsmen and failed to stimulate popular interest in the sport. Mass production, on the other hand, lowered the per boat cost, which, in turn, attracted more participants.

Unlike yachts built for open classes, one-designs depreciate less because they will not be out-built in subsequent years, so older boats can continue to race actively for years. Frequently, when significant changes are made in the class, such as an alteration of the rig or a switch to fiberglass hulls, the change is simultaneously made throughout the class, or restrictions keep the old boats on a competitive level with the newer ones. A class association regulating and promoting the racing of these boats encourages more to join the competition and spreads the interest geographically, in some cases to the point of international competition. In addition, one-designs make handicapping rules redundant and leave fewer opportunities to circumvent rules.

The sailing and racing of small craft for pleasure began before the 1870s. The earliest one-design races in America took place in the resort town of North Haven, Maine, in 1887. Dr. Charles C.

Weld of Boston designed 14-1/2-foot open dinghies for the purpose in 1884, and the first two were built by a local New Haven, Connecticut, boatbuilder. After several more were built, the 1887 race was held, which Miss Ellen Hayward won on *Guffin*. The North Haven dinghies survived for their 70th anniversary regatta in 1957, with 27 boats participating.

Another early one-design class was an adaptation of a New Jersey gunning boat, the Barnegat Bay Sneakbox (see chapter on gunning boats). The spoon-shaped hull of these boats was designed for duck hunting in either shallow marshes or rough waters. Later, Howard Perrine drew the formal design for the racing class, a 15-foot, gaff-rigged centerboard sloop. A 14-foot successor to his design long remained as a modern racing class on Barnegat Bay.

In the early 20th century, individual yacht clubs would order a small fleet of one-designs, but these types remained largely local, or occasionally regional, as in the case of the Barnegat Bay Sneakboxes. Only with the appearance of the Star class did a one-design boat receive widespread recognition, a process replicated many times, beginning in the 1930s.

The Star class was the first one-design to gain widespread popularity. The design was produced in 1911 by Francis Sweisguth of the Manhattan naval architecture firm of Gardner and Co. at the request of George A. Corry, a small boat skipper from Port Washington, Long Island. Sweisguth expanded a 1907 design by William Gardner, the "Bug," to produce the Star. Isaac Smith of Port Washington built the first 22 in 1911 for $260 per boat, and the first race was held the same year. Eleven more Stars were built in Nahant, Massachusetts, which were first known as "Nahant Bugs." A slightly larger version of the Star, the "Fish," was introduced in 1913, but neither the

SPECIFICATIONS

Length over all	20' 0"
Length water line	15' 7"
Draft, board up	1' 7"
Draft, board down	4' 5"
Beam	6' 7"
Sail Area	247 sq. ft.
Weight, approx.	800 lbs.
Spars	Hollow spruce
Rudder	Pivoting
Hardware	All bronze
Rigging	Stainless steel

Get a Twenty

THE SMARTEST BOAT YOU WILL EVER SAIL

You may own larger and far more expensive yachts, but you will never sail one with more "life" than a Hartge built Chesapeake Twenty. The way that she responds to the light cats paws or leaps ahead when struck with a heavy flaw reminds you of a thoroughbred race horse. No true racing skipper can ever sail this boat without falling in love with her. She is the boat you have always dreamed of owning— a happy ship, taking all weather in her stride. She will never let you down.

ERNEST H. HARTGE
Designer & Builder
GALESVILLE, MD.

Ernest H. Hartge's promotional literature for the Chesapeake 20.

Bug nor the Fish attracted much attention.

The Star class was the first of the one-designs to gain the sponsorship of a class organization. The Star Class Association of America was founded early in 1915, and George Corry became its first commodore. His successor, George W. Elder, started Star fleets on Great South Bay, Chesapeake Bay, and Lake Erie, and in New Orleans, Southern California, and Chicago in the years following World War I. The first class championship was held in 1922 on Long Island Sound. The class added "international" to its name in 1923 when a fleet was established in British Columbia.

The first Star boat fleet chartered on the Chesapeake was at the Gibson Island Club on the Western Shore of Maryland, shortly after that club acquired its first twelve Stars. Later that year, a second fleet was chartered at Hampton Roads, Virginia. By 1924, Stars could also be found racing near St. Michaels, in the annual regatta of the Miles River Yacht Club. Both on the Chesapeake and elsewhere, class organizations were vital to the geographical spread and the longevity of one-design classes. The success of the Star was ultimately marked by its inclusion as an Olympic class for sailboat racing from 1932 to 1968. During the Depression, Star boat racing declined on the Bay, though this was offset in part by the addition of new Star fleets at Elk River and on the Eastern Shore.

Several changes were made in the class design. The rig was originally a "sliding gunter," a gaff sail with the yard nearly on the vertical. The mast was stepped well forward and the boom extended beyond the stern. In 1921, a Marconi rig of similar proportions was adopted, eliminating the long yard. The rig was altered once again in 1929 and called for a taller main with a shorter foot, and a jib with a little more hoist. The Stars permit no genoa or spinnaker, and allow no more than 280 square feet of sail on a stayed mast. Although the Star Association was comparatively late in doing so, it accepted a fiberglass version of the hull in the late 1960s.

By the 1930s, several new designs appeared, including the Snipe and the Comet, the latter designed by C. Lowndes Johnson (1881-1971), a Star class racer with the Gibson Island fleet who also designed a training scow, the LJ class, for junior racing at the Gibson Island Club. Lowndes and his brother, Graham, had won the Chesa-peake Bay Star Class Championship for three consecutive years, and in 1929 the Johnson boys became the only Chesapeake Bay sailors ever to win the International Star Class Yacht Racing Championship, held that year in New Orleans.

Several classes of racing dinghies also appeared, and among the more popular were the Penguins, designed in 1939 and initially intended for wintertime off-season races known as "frostbite regattas." The first "frostbite regatta" was held on 2 January 1932 on Manhasset Bay, off Port Washington, Long Island, and "frostbiters" quickly caught on as an off-season racing event. Rufus G. Smith wrote an article for the May 1940 issue of *Yachting* magazine that popularized the Penguin class, and a national class was organized that fall in Alexandria, Virginia. Penguins subsequently became the most popular dinghy class, and one of the most popular one-designs.

After the Second World War, an explosion of interest in one-design racing took place, following the introduction of fiberglass hulls, which reduced the cost of the boats. Star boats continued to enjoy success, but shared the waters with a growing number of nationally and internationally recognized one-design classes.

Most of the one-design boats in the collection of the Chesapeake Bay Maritime Museum are of hard-chine construction. Boats of this type such as the Stars, Comets, and Penguins were intended for construction in wood, by amateurs at home. This was also the case with the Museum's racing scow.

The Chesapeake 20s, on the other hand, were round-bottom boats designed for greater speed and requiring the building skills of a professional. Designed and first built in 1937, these swift boats were not members of a strictly one-design class, but of a restricted or developmental class; builders had some freedom to alter aspects of boats in the class, within limits set by the class organization.

All of the boats described in this section are small racing craft, designed with the intention of creating fair and close competition among those who sailed and raced them. In each case, they were intended mainly for amateur captains and crews, and often for amateur builders as well. One-design racing in small craft remains popular today and, while several of the design types in the Museum have disappeared from competition, others continue to be actively raced.

St. Michael's scow, 1937.

St. Michaels Sailing Scow

Built 1931, Baltimore, Maryland,
by Herbert Barnes Aldrich
12' x 4'

The St. Michaels Sailing Scows began racing as a loosely organized local class in the regattas of the Miles River Yacht Club, where they raced from 1926 to 1939. At first, the only class rules were a 12-foot limit and a requirement that they be genuine scows: flat-bottomed and blunt-ended. A "St. Michaels Sailing Scow Free For All Class" was added for boats that did not comply. They were rigged as gaff sloops, some with short sprits to extend the jib forward.

The class was started by Commodore Nick Hardcastle, who encouraged and promoted the junior sailing program at the Miles River Yacht Club. In 1929, George Krill made official drawings to standardize the class; these called for a Marconi rig carrying 100 square feet of sail. The sailing scow in the collection was built to the George Krill plans.

Two scows built by John B. Harrison, of Tilghman Island, variations on the St. Michaels

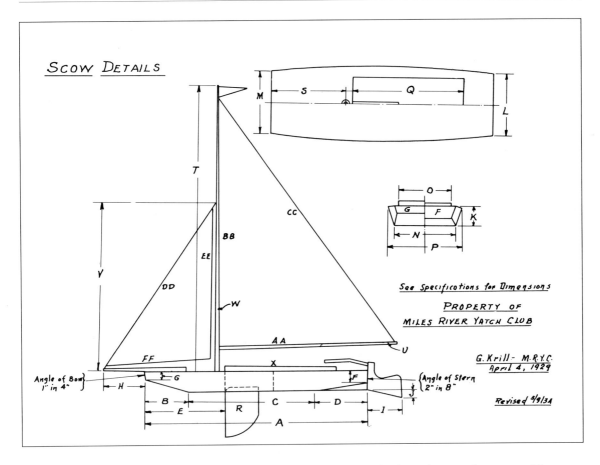

Scow Details

See Specifications for Dimensions

PROPERTY OF
MILES RIVER YACHT CLUB

G. Krill - M.R.Y.C.
April 4, 1929

Revised 4/9/31

scow, with reverse arc bottoms, lightweight spars, and V-shaped centerboard trunks, were so successful against the largely home-built scows that they were outlawed from the class.

The class never contained many boats, and only a handful of scows regularly sailed in the regattas through the late 1930s.

H. B. Aldrich built the Museum's scow for his sons, Walter and Ralph, in the garage at his house on Overland Avenue in Baltimore. Because Mrs. Aldrich disapproved of the project, Aldrich and his sons completed the job in two weeks, while she was away on a trip.

The brothers kept the scow on San Domingo Creek, near St. Michaels, during the summer, so the planks would swell and keep the bottom tight. During this time, the boys would camp on Elmer Hamilton's property on Pea Neck Road in St. Michaels, where they had built two docks. Their first cousin, John Aldrich, also stayed there and kept a scow his father had built for him. The scows were taken to the Miles River for regattas where the H. B. Aldrich scow won a number of races. This scow is heavily built, with a cross-planked flat bottom, open cockpit, and small centerboard well. The flat bottom rises at either end, a little

higher in the bow than at the stern. The mast passes through a square opening in the deck. The St. Michaels Sailing Scows were reportedly difficult to handle and could not sail very close to the wind. However, the Aldrichs, whose participation made the continuation of the class possible for many years in the 1930s, remember the boats as good, fast sailers that were easily righted when capsized. Only two surviving examples remain, this and one of the scows built by John B. Harrison.

Donors: H. B. and R. C. Aldrich

67-144-1

Judy after restoration, 1984.

Judy
Penguin Class No. 1

Built 1939, Arlington, Virginia,
by William W. Heintz
11' 6" x 4' 7"

In the fall of 1938, William W. Heintz and several other Potomac River sailors began to search for an inexpensive and easy-to-build boat for racing in frostbite regattas. They selected a design by Philip L. Rhodes. In 1933 they had rejected a similar design by Rhodes in favor of the Dyer Dhow by Bill Dyer. Rhodes's 1939 reworked design, however, became the most popular racing dinghy class after it was accepted by the Potomac River Sailors of Alexandria, Virginia.

Penguins were intended especially for frostbite regattas and were given the name by May Heintz, wife of builder Bill Heintz, for the flightless bird that thrives in ice and cold water.

The first six Penguins were built by Bill Heintz and Ralph Youngs in the winter and spring of 1939 and, by the summer, 12 or 13 were racing on the Potomac. *Judy*, named for Bill Heintz's infant daughter, was the first of the fleet. The builder explained her color scheme: "*Judy*, being the first boat, was painted like a penguin with black topsides, white bottom and white inside. (I added the red boot stripe for decoration.)" *Judy* retains her resemblance to the Antarctic bird today, though she no longer races.

The Heintz family raced *Judy* on the Chesapeake Bay until the early 1950s, when she was stored on account of a leaky hull. In 1965, the plywood dinghy was fiberglassed and returned to racing, but the fiberglass made her too heavy to compete with the newer Penguins. Typical Penguins weigh only 140 pounds, making them easy to transport on cartops or trailers. They are generally raced with two crew members, though the single 72-square-foot sail is designed to allow the boats to be sailed single-handedly.

During her restoration, to save *Judy*'s original, delaminated plywood, the Museum restorers injected epoxy into the separated layers. She retains her fiberglass from the 1965 rebuilding, and her spars are intact.

Donor: William W. Heintz

71-54-1

Zoea
Comet Class No. 1

Built 1932, Oxford, Maryland, by Ralph Wiley
15' 9" x 5' 0"

Zoea **with Tom Martin at the helm, and Maria Wheeler. Photograph by H. R. Hollyday.**

The Comet was designed in 1932 by C. Lowndes Johnson at the request of Mrs. Elliot Wheeler of Oxford, who wanted a small, fast boat that would also be easy to handle for her sons, David and Thomas Martin. Lowndes Johnson designed a shoal draft centerboard sloop similar to the larger Star class keel boats in which he and his brother had been international champions. *Zoea* was built at the Ralph Wiley Boatyard to a slightly altered design. Though Lowndes Johnson built many Star class boats, no Comets were ever built at his shop on Miles River Neck.

The plans for this one-design centerboard sloop appeared in the March 1932 issue of *Yachting* magazine. These boats, known at first as "Crabs," gained further popularity when one was displayed at the 1933 New York Boat Show, where it was called a "Star Junior." In 1935, after several fleets had formed, a national organization was established which adopted the name "Comet" for the new class, from the desire to use a name related to the "Star." The earlier design name "Crab" explains the origin of the name *Zoea*: a zoea is a crab larva.

Although *Zoea* varied in several measurements from the standard class design, mainly a 1-1/2-inch difference in length, she was accepted as a Comet. Because many of the early Comets were home-built by amateurs, other Comets exhibited similar variations, but were accepted as legitimate.

Zoea raced for many years on the Tred Avon River near Oxford with Thomas Martin or his mother, Maria D. Wheeler, at the helm, but never gained a national or international championship. Lowndes Johnson is also known to have sailed *Zoea*.

Since 1946 *Zoea* has passed through several owners, mainly in Talbot County, Maryland, but later in New Jersey. In 1962, Fletcher Marine Products of Westmont, New Jersey, enlarged *Zoea's* cockpit and skeg; at the same time, her spars were replaced.

Zoea has several construction details of interest. When her restoration at the Museum began, structural problems were found with her side frames, which had cracked where they met the bottom frames at the chine. Her deck beams are located directly over the bottom frames, and many of the side frames were bolted to the after side of the deck beam and the forward side of the bottom frame. This twist evidently caused the side frames to crack. When the cedar side frames were replaced, a bevel was cut at each end to avoid placing a twisting strain on the member.

When the cockpit was enlarged in 1962, the deck beams around the cockpit were sistered, and several of the cedar deck planks immediately outboard of the cockpit were replaced. At some time, the mahogany rubrail was replaced.

Donor: Daniel P. Barnard IV

69-59-1

Escape
Star Class, No. 1444

Built 1937, Easton, Maryland, by C. Lowndes Johnson
22' 8-1/2" x 5' 8-1/4"

The Star boats built by Lowndes Johnson of Easton, Maryland, played an important role in the history of Star class racing on the Chesapeake. He is known to have built at least seven, which bore the names *Undine*, *Sailfish*, *Eel*, *Ripple*, *White Cap*, *Wave* and *Escape*. Johnson's younger brother, Graham, assisted in the construction of the first four before he died of a heart attack at the tiller of a Star boat off Oxford in 1931.

The Johnson boys, racing for the Gibson Island Club, became the most successful Star boat team on the Chesapeake shortly after they started Star boat sailing in 1927. In 1928, having won the fleet and Chesapeake Bay Challenge trophies, the Johnson boys (Graham was always the skipper) travelled to the west coast for the World Championship races, where they placed sixth in *Undine*. The following year, the Johnsons again captured the Chesapeake Bay Championships, this

Star boat Escape, *a Comet, and LJ No. 1 becalmed.*

time in their Star boat *Eel*. Later they won the World Championship in New Orleans, the only Chesapeake Bay sailors ever to do so. This brought the championship series to Gibson Island in 1930 and, though the brothers won on the Bay for the third consecutive year in *Ripple*, they failed to keep the World Championship.

In 1937 Melville Bell Grosvenor had Lowndes Johnson build a seventh Star of cedar on sawn oak frames. It was named *Escape*, and given hull number 1444. Grosvenor, with his wife Helen, won the Chesapeake Bay Elimination Series in *Escape* in 1937 and 1938. When the Grosvenors took *Escape* up to Long Island Sound for the international championships, her trailer broke loose from the car, and *Escape*, carried stern first on her trailer, struck a pole which damaged the port side of the transom. The patch on the transom from this accident is still visible.

Escape is in good condition but is unrestored.

Donor: Rodney L. Harrison

82-10-1

Ripple, Star class boat, under construction at Lowndes Johnson's boatshop, circa 1932. Johnson built at least seven Star boats, including Escape.

Riptide, first across the line in the Annapolis to Gibson Island Race, 1942. Crew are John A. Coughlin (owner/skipper), John Kramer and Ed Coughlin.

Riptide
Chesapeake 20

Built circa 1938, Galesville, Maryland, by Ernest H. ("Dick") Hartge
20' x 6' 7"

The Chesapeake 20 class was designed for the shallow, calm waters of West River, south of Annapolis. This was an open class, but Hartge built about 30 of the 20-foot sloops to a single design, of which *Riptide* is an early example, reportedly the third. After the Second World War, Hartge stopped building the centerboard sloops because of the increasing expense of the boats and competition from cheaper fiberglass models. Several other 20-footers raced in the class, as many as 75 in the 1940s.

The Chesapeake 20s were heavily canvassed, carrying 247 square feet of sail, so they typically required a crew of five. At 800 pounds, the wooden boats were fairly lightweight for boats of their length.

Riptide was built about 1938 for Mr. "Midge" Phillips of Eastport, Maryland. Hartge kept no written records of the boats he built, and the class was only loosely organized, so it is not possible to firmly establish many of the details of *Riptide*'s early history.

There were two divisions in the class, Division I being the round-chine Chesapeake 20s. *Vanity* is known to be the first of this design. A slightly earlier variation on the design was a hard chine 20-footer with a transom, the first of which was *Seawitch*. These hard chine boats formed Division II of the class. *Seawitch* was an improvement on the double-ender *Albatross* design, published in the November 1936 *Yachting*. At least four boats were built to the *Seawitch* design, which was sailed as a restricted class.

The Chesapeake 20s are planked with cedar over ash frames. Oak is used to back the transom and for the stern knee. The rudder, transom face, centerboard bed logs, centerboard and trim are all of mahogany, and spruce is used for the hollow spar.

Riptide's lightweight wooden hull had been covered with fiberglass, which was replaced during a restoration at the Hartge Yacht Yard in 1978-1979.

Donors: Mr. and Mrs. H. C. Wright, Jr.

71-31-1

Hampton Class No. 539

Built 1955, Arlington, Virginia,
by Fred Brister & family
18' x 5' 9-1/2"

In 1934, the Hampton Yacht Club Racing Association of Hampton, Virginia, asked Vincent Serio, also of Hampton, to design a fast, light, shoal draft, one-design boat. The following year he built the first Hamptons at the Hampton Roads Boat Works in Newport News, Virginia. Serio built nearly 600 wooden Hamptons before his retirement in the early 1960s. Eddie Williams and others then assumed responsibility for building the boats, first intending to continue working in wood, but deciding instead to make molded fiberglass hulls. Williams has since made over 100 of the fiberglass sloops. To keep the old wooden Hamptons competitive with the fiberglass boats, class rules require that the square-foot density of fiberglass hulls equals that of the red cedar boats.

The design became popular throughout the Chesapeake Bay, but in recent years, most of the racing has been done in Tidewater Virginia.

Hamptons have a V-bottom and a hard chine, making them attractive to amateur builders. Serio catered to this interest by providing kits, and number 539 was assembled from one of these. Aside from Serio, several other professionals also built Hamptons, including Dorr Willey of Riverside Boat Works, Elizabeth City, North Carolina; David W. Brown of Hampton, Virginia; and Jim Richardson, Cambridge, Maryland. Fred Brister and his family built theirs in their backyard in 1955 with a kit bought from Vincent Serio. Serio included the structural members in the kit, and plans for the jig. Planking, fittings, and rig had to be bought separately.

Hampton number 539 is decked and planked with cedar over mahogany frames and spruce deck beams. Her keel, transom, rudder, coaming, rub rail, sheer stringer, and the cap on her centerboard well are all of Philippine mahogany. The centerboard is of 1/4-inch plate aluminum. Her 25-foot, 6-inch solid spruce mast with a single spreader, raked aft at 1/2 inch per foot, supports 149.8 square feet of sail. Mr. Brister recalls buying the pear-shaped mast and the plank boom from Serio. The first rig on number 539 was the old "telephone pole" rig, with three fixed stays. Later, sliding backstays and a trapeze were added.

The builder and skipper of number 539 described her as an average Hampton, neither particularly fast nor slow. She was first used as a summer

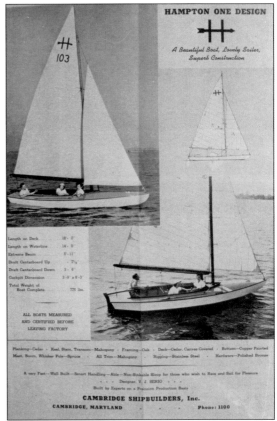

Several Chesapeake builders made Hamptons including Cambridge Shipbuilders of Cambridge, MD.

daysailer on the Rhode River, where she was kept in the water. When Brister, with his daughter crewing, started to race in regattas on the Potomac, the Hampton was kept ashore as a "dry boat." At that time Brister routed out the bottom seams and installed cedar splines.

Donor: Fred Brister

76-6-1

Hampton No. 539 on exhibit at CBMM, 1992.

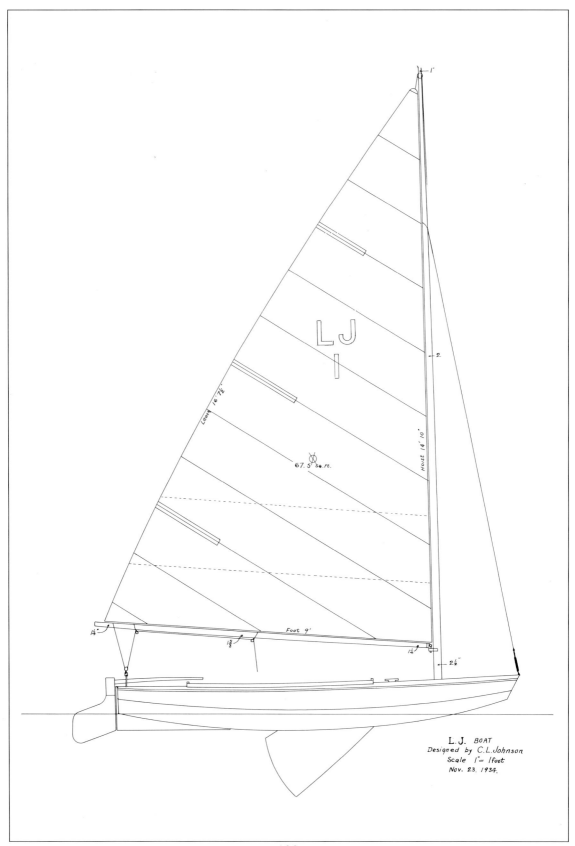

Leach 16'-7½"

Hoist 14'-10½"

67.5 sq. ft.

Foot 9'

L.J. BOAT
Designed by C.L.Johnson
Scale 1"= 1foot
Nov. 23. 1934.

LJ Class No. 88

Built circa 1947-1948, Baltimore, Maryland,
by John L. Flanigan, Jr. and
William Patrick Flanigan
11' x 4'

Lowndes Johnson, well-known boatbuilder, Star class racer, and designer of the Comet class, also designed the smaller LJ class. These small, V-bottom centerboard scow sloops were designed as a junior training class for the Yacht Squadron at the Gibson Island Club, located south of Baltimore on the Chesapeake Bay. They were reputedly excellent for teaching sailing. In 1935 the class took hold at Gibson Island and the LJ's were first mentioned as a class in sailing awards the same year.

John L. Flanigan, Jr., who had sailed LJ scow sloops as a youth, enlisted the help of his cousin, William Patrick Flanigan, to build two LJ sloops. One was built for John Flanigan's family, which once owned three LJ scows; the other for his cousin's children. These were among the last boats built in the class, which was soon superseded by the Penguins at Gibson Island because Penguins were considerably cheaper to build and could be competitively raced by adults.

John Flanigan arbitrarily attached the number 88 to his boat and, like the other sail numbers in the class, no sequence was implied. She has not been restored, but is in good condition. The LJ class carried a 67.5 square foot mainsail and no jib.

In 1949, Lowndes Johnson designed a 13-foot, 10-inch version for the Gibson Island juniors who had learned on the smaller craft and wished to try a larger boat, but could not afford an expensive Comet. The plans for the "LJ Sr." appeared in the January 1949 issue of *The Rudder*. The larger LJ carried 96 square feet of sail.

Donor: John L. Flanigan, Jr.

72-25-1

MISCELLANEOUS BOATS

C. Lowndes Johnson's iceboat is the only boat in the Museum's collection which does not fit into any of the other categories.

Iceboat

Built before 1918, Miles River Neck, Maryland, by C. Lowndes Johnson
20' 0" x 12' 0"

Lowndes Johnson built this iceboat for his own use, sometime between 1910 and 1918. The design may have come from *The Rudder*, to which he and his brother, Graham, subscribed.

The keel measures 2 inches by 6 inches and is braced through the middle with 1- by 6-inch boards on either side, 8 feet long. The runner plank is a heavy beam, 9 inches by 3 inches, attached at a perpendicular to the keel, slightly forward of center. Diagonal braces of 2 inches by 4 inches hold the runner plank to the keel.

The boat rests on three runners, one at either end of the runner plank of 40-inch length, and a third, acting as the rudder, under the after end of the keel. In each case, the runner is a V-shaped strip of iron mounted on the underside of a wooden "shoe," which sweeps upward at the forward end. The stern rudder marks this iceboat as one of the older "stern steering" variety. Atop the frame and just forward of the rudder rests the 7-foot long cockpit.

A gaff-rigged sail was attached to a 16-foot mast, the latter stayed with heavy gauge wire shrouds and a single spreader, and stepped forward of the runner plank. The sail appears to have been made from two old sails patched together. A club footed jib completed the sail plan.

John G. Earle of Easton, Maryland, remembers sailing this craft on the frozen Miles River in the winter of 1917-1918.

Donor: C. Lowndes Johnson

66-47-1

Iceboat built by C. Lowndes Johnson.

SMALL CRAFT COLLECTION

Year Acquired	Name	Type	Accession Number	Page
1963		Five-Log Tilghman Canoe	63-1-1	26
1965		Single-Log Dugout	65-127-1	19
1966		Rail Skiff	66-2-1	104
1966		Bushwhack Boat	66-20-1	93
1966	GHOST	Deadrise Skiff	66-22-1	56
1966		Iceboat	66-47-1	122
1966		Delaware Ducker	66-199-1	98
1967		Sinkbox (Double-body)	67-67-1	89
1967	MERRY WIDOW	Three-Log Poquoson Canoe	67-129-1	22
1967		St. Michaels Sailing Scow	67-144-1	112
1967	EDNA E. LOCKWOOD	Nine-Log Bugeye	67-155-1	34
1968		Bushwhack Boat (Sneakboat)	68-52-1	92
1968		Single-Log Dugout	68-84-1	19
1968		Yankee Skiff (Staten Island Skiff)	68-116-1	38
1968	MARIANNE	Three-Log Tilghman Canoe	68-124-1	21
1969	LILLIAN R.	Five-Log Pocomoke Canoe	69-41-1	28
1969	ZOEA	Comet Class No. 1	69-59-1	115
1969	LARK	Sailing Skiff	69-74-1	60
1969		Rail Skiff	69-97-1	103
1970		Gilling Skiff (Shad Skiff)	70-76-1	40
1970		Pound-Net Skiff	70-82-1	78
1971		Pilot's Gig	71-34-1	43
1971	RIPTIDE	Chesapeake 20	71-31-1	118
1971	JUDY	Penguin Class No. 1	71-54-1	114
1972		LJ Class No. 88	72-25-1	121
1972		Crabbing Skiff	72-31-1	50
1973		Sneakbox	73-25-1	96
1973	W.A. JOHNS	Three-Log Canoe	73-27-1	20
1973		Sneakskiff	73-54-1	109
1973		Sinkbox (Single-body)	73-54-2	87
1974		Double-Ended Sailing Skiff	74-12-1	48
1974		Striker Boat	74-15-1	42
1974		Gunning Skiff	74-18-1	107
1974		Sneakbox	74-31-1	96
1974		Icebox	74-31-2	90
1974	MINNIE G.	Hooper Island Launch	74-45-1	65
1975		Sneakskiff (Lighting Skiff)	75-24-1	109
1975		Smith Island Power Crabbing Skiff	75-25-1	52
1975		Sinkbox (Sit-down model)	75-26-1	89

Year Acquired	Name	Type	Accession Number	Page
1975		Sinkbox (Single-body)	75-30-1	88
1975		Icebox	75-30-2	90
1975		Sneakbox	75-30-3	95
1975	ROSIE PARKS	Two Sail Bateau (Skipjack)	75-53-1	70
1976		Hampton Class No. 539	76-6-1	119
1977		Pram	77-11-1	80
1977	LORRAINE	Gilling Skiff (Shad Skiff)	77-25-1	41
1978	SUMMER DUCK	Rail Skiff	78-14-1	106
1978		Delaware Ducker	78-24-1	100
1978	AVA	Sailing Skiff	78-34-1	55
1979		Rail Skiff	79-2-1	105
1979	PC	Motorized Sinkbox Tender	79-38-1	91
1979		Gunning Garvey Box	79-39-1	101
1981		Sailing Skiff	81-11-1	54
1981	WIDGEON	Sailing & Rowing Skiff	81-27-1	82
1970	ALVERTA	Five-Log Canoe	81-29-1	30
1982	ESCAPE	Star Class No. 1444	82-10-1	116
1982	DECOY	Pram	82-11-1	81
1982	BESSIE LEE	Seaside Bateau	82-14-1	58
1983	MARTHA	Hooper Island Launch	83-19-1	66
1984	ATROPOS	Barnegat Bay Sneakbox	84-11-1	94
1984		Sharptown Barge	84-18-1	76
1984		Rail Skiff	84-21-1	102
1984	OLD POINT	Seven-Log Crab Dredger	84-30-1	32
1985	FLY	Five-Log Poquoson Canoe	85-2-1	24
1986		Delaware Ducker	86-43-1	100
1987	SHOREBIRD	Crab Scrape	87-49-1	64
1988		Three-Log Power Canoe	88-25-1	23
1988		Potomac River Dory	88-43-1	62
1989	SHUTTLECOCK	Utility Runabout	89-7-1	67
1989		Pushboat	89-8-1	84
1989		Deadrise Sloop	89-19-1	68
1989		Choptank River Shad Skiff	89-20-1	74
1989	KATE D.	Five-Log Canoe	89-34-1	25
1989		Sharptown Barge	89-30-1	75
1991	DELAWARE	Tug	91-3-1	44
1991		Potomac River Dory	91-4-1	61

GLOSSARY

Athwartships – perpendicular to the centerline of a boat.

Bateau – on the Chesapeake, a skipjack, or any V-bottom (deadrise) boat larger than a skiff.

Bermuda rig – 20th-century term for a sail plan with jib-headed (triangular) sails, arranged fore and aft. Each sail is set with a single halyard. This rig requires no gaff, but a taller mast is required than for a gaff sail.

Brogan – a Chesapeake Bay log bottom workboat, larger than a log canoe but smaller than a bugeye (usually 40' to 45'). These two-masted craft were partially decked with a small cuddy cabin forward, and were often used to oyster with patent tongs.

Bugeye (Buckeye) – perhaps from "buckie," Scottish for oyster. An enlarged and decked log canoe (30' to 80') with jib-headed sails on two stayed masts, and with a large cabin aft. Later examples were frame-built, often with round sterns as opposed to the sharp-ended log bugeye. A few bugeyes carried a single mast.

Camber – the curvature of a deck to shed the water. Standard camber for weather decks is 1/50 the vessel's breadth.

Carvel built – planks laid edge on and caulked to make them water-tight, giving a smooth surface to the hull.

Centerboard – a movable keel made of wood or metal within a well, or slot, in the bottom of a vessel that may be raised or lowered to reduce leeway to a minimum.

Ceiling – inside planking, fastened to inner surface of frames, forming an inner skin.

Chine – (often pronounced "chime") line of intersection between the sides and bottom of a V- or flat-bottom boat. The chine piece, or chine log runs stem to stern on the inside of the planking along this intersection.

Chunk – a piece of a hull carved from a timber. A "chunkboat" is a log-bottom boat, built of several "chunks" or logs. Log canoes were sometimes described as "chunk-built."

Deadrise – 1. also called rise of floor. The amount of bottom rise from keel to chine. The amount of deadrise can be measured both by angle in degrees and in feet. 2. any V-bottom Chesapeake Bay boat; today most commonly applied to V-bottom workboats.

Harpin, Harping – on a Barnegat Bay sneakbox, a curved horizontal wood strip inside the seam where the bottom meets the deck. Because there is no stem in a sneak box, the harpin provides a structural member for fastening the forward end of the bottom planks to the deck planks.

Horse (Deckhorse) – a low iron rod or wooden spar parallel to the deck along which the traveller for the sheet of a fore-and-aft sail may shift from side to side when tacking.

Keel – the main structural member or "backbone" of a vessel, running longitudinally along the centerline of the bottom.

Keelson – fore-and-aft member usually on or above the keel, or on top of the floor timbers, and fastened through floors and keel.

Ketch – a sailing vessel rigged with two masts, the forward mast being the taller and the after mast forward of the intersection of the rudder post and the waterline. On Chesapeake Bay boats, these masts are designated fore and main (in schooner fashion) instead of main and mizzen, as they are customarily called elsewhere.

Lapstrake built – (sometimes called clinker-built) planks are laid over the frames so that the bottom of the upper strake laps over the top of the strake below. Lapstrake construction is not common to the Chesapeake Bay.

Leg-of-Mutton sail – a fore-and-aft sail of triangular shape set abaft the mast. Also called a Bermuda-rigged sail or a jib-headed sail.

Log Canoe – on the Chesapeake Bay, any open boat (12' to 40'), built of one to seven carved logs, sharp at each end, sometimes with topsides framed and planked. A few racing canoes were built with transom sterns. Usually rigged with one or two jib-headed spritsails, with or without jib, set on sharply raking, unstayed pole masts.

Marconi rig – a sail plan characterized by a jib-headed sail set on a mast, without a yard or gaff (see also Bermuda rig).

Monkey rail – a light rail above the main rail that runs along the bulwarks and across the stern.

Overall length – the extreme length of a hull, from the outboard end of the stempost to the outboard end of the sternpost.

Oyster Dredge – (pronounced "drudge") a short woven twine and chain bag attached to a rectangular steel frame. Long side of frame has steel teeth that dig into the seabed when pulled by a dredge boat.

Oyster Tongs – wooden shafted tongs, 12' to 32' long, bearing opposing, pincer-like baskets, used for gathering oysters in shallow waters.

Patent Tongs – (deep water tongs) large capacity, mechanically operated oyster tongs for use in waters too deep for hand tonging. The earliest and most widely used design was patented in 1887 by Charles L. Marsh of Solomons Island.

Pungy – a Chesapeake Bay vessel with schooner rig, but generally carrying a single large jib. Pungies are deeper at the stern than bow, and with the greatest beam well forward of 'midships. The rig is taller and lighter than that of an ordinary schooner, with sails set on sharply raking masts. A "she-pungy" had a centerboard.

Push Boat – a heavily built yawl boat with a large engine used to propel an unpowered sailing vessel. Push boats are typically carried on Maryland oyster dredgeboats, where law regulates dredging under power (see also yawl boat).

Rabbet – a channel or groove cut along the edge or face of a timber (usually a stem or keel) to receive the edge of a plank fitted to it.

Rocker – the curvature of a keel from 'midships toward each end.

Sheer – the curvature of the edge of a vessel's deck from about midships toward each end.

Sister – A part of a structural member (frame, keelson, clamp, or bilge stringer) placed alongside another, usually as a means of repairing or rebuilding a vessel.

Skeg – (pronounced "skrag" on some parts of the Chesapeake Bay) deadwood or a plank under the stern, which may provide lateral resistance and directional stability.

Skipjack (two-sail bateau) – a sailing vessel built with deadrise construction, decked, and with a cabin. Skipjacks generally carry a triangular mainsail and jib, set on a sharply raking mast. A few two-masted skipjacks, or "three-sail bateaux" were built. Only type of vessel still used for oyster dredging in Maryland.

Sliding Gunter Rig – a sail plan in which a triangular sail is set with the lower part of the luff attached to the mast and the upper part to a yard that is hoisted aloft as an extension of the mast.

Sprit – 1. a small spar extending from the foot of the mast to the peak of a quadrilateral fore-and-aft sail for the purpose of extending the sail, and secured to the mast by a line called a snotter or stirrup. 2. on the Chesapeake, a sprit (pronounced "spreet") is commonly used on a log canoe to extend the clew of a jib-headed sail. It extends horizontally and is secured to the mast in sprit fashion, functioning in place of a boom.

Squatboards (settling boards) – horizontal or nearly horizontal boards or plates attached to the underside of the stern on powered boats lacking a sufficiently deep hull at the stern to prevent squatting or settling under power. Especially seen on workboats whose hull types are taken from sailing models.

Sternpost – a structural member extending up from the after end of the keel. On the Chesapeake Bay, it may be called a "paddlepost." A false sternpost has no structural function, but may serve to mount the rudder hardware.

Stool – a group of decoys, typically anchored in an arrangement around or near a blind or gunning boat, to attract waterfowl.

Strake – a line of planking parallel to the keel running the length of the hull. The garboard strake abuts the keel.

Strongback – on the Chesapeake, especially in deadrise boats, a heavy frame at right angles to the keel, usually running from one chine to the opposite one.

Transom stern – "square" or "flat" stern, usually sloping outward from the sternpost, as distinguished from the sharp or round stern. A form of stern in which the upper part of the hull terminates in a large, flat surface, that is square to the central longitudinal (and horizontal) plane.

Washboard – on the Chesapeake, the side deck or horizontal plank inboard of the gunwale on a low freeboard sailing craft or a workboat. The washboards on an oyster tonging boat had to be wide enough to accommodate the feet of the waterman while working the tongs.

Waterman – on the Chesapeake, a fisherman who catches fish, oysters, crabs, clams, or other seafood.

Yawl Boat – a small boat generally carried on stern davits of Chesapeake Bay schooners, bugeyes, skipjacks, etc. A push boat is a type of yawl boat that developed in the early 20th century (see also push boat).

SELECTED BIBLIOGRAPHY

General Reference

Anderson, Richard K., Jr. *Guidelines for Recording Historic Ships.* Washington, D.C.: National Park Service, US Dept. of the Interior, 1988.

Baker, William A. "The Preservation of Chesapeake Bay Watercraft." Address to the Chesapeake Sailing Yacht Symposium, Annapolis, MD, 1977.

Bray, Maynard. *Mystic Seaport Museum Watercraft.* Mystic, CT: Mystic Seaport Museum, 1979.

Brewington, M.V. *Chesapeake Bay, A Pictorial Maritime History.* Cambridge, MD: Cornell Maritime Press, 1956.

Burgess, Robert H. *Chesapeake Sailing Craft, Part 1.* Cambridge, MD: Tidewater Publishers, 1975.

_____. *Chesapeake Circle.* Cambridge, MD: Cornell Maritime Press, 1965.

_____. *This Was Chesapeake Bay.* Cambridge, MD: Cornell Maritime Press, 1963.

Chapelle, Howard I. *American Small Sailing Craft.* New York: W.W. Norton & Co., 1951.

_____. *The National Watercraft Collection.* Washington, D.C.: GPO, 1960.

"Chesapeake Craft." *Forest and Stream* 22 (Jul. 1884). n.p.

Chowning, Larry S. *Harvesting the Chesapeake -Tools and Traditions.* Centreville, MD: Tidewater Publishers, 1990.

Dilley, Ray. "Skifts, Skrags and Collars Mark Lingo of Chesapeake Waterman." *National Fisherman* 62 (Jul. 1981), 73-5.

Douty, J.F. "History of Chesapeake Sailing Vessels." Chesapeake Section, Society of Naval Architects and Marine Engineers. Washington, D.C.: 29 Nov. 1951.

Gardner, John. *Building Classic Small Craft.* Camden, ME: International Marine Publishing Co., 1977.

Gibson, R. Hammond. *Eastern Shore Chips and Shavings.* St.Michaels, MD: Chesapeake Bay Maritime Museum, 1979.

Goode, George Brown. *The Fisheries and Fishery Industries of the United States.* Washington, D.C.: GPO, 1887.

Hall, Henry. *Report on the Ship-Building Industry of the United States.* 10th Census. Washington, D.C.: GPO, 1884.

Johnson, Paula J., ed. *Working the Water: The Commercial Fisheries of Maryland's Patuxent River.* Charlottesville, VA: The University Press of Virginia, 1988.

Morris, E.P. *The Fore-and-Aft Rig in America.* New Haven: Yale University Press, 1927.

Nabb, Edward H. "Chesapeake Bay Dredge Boats." *The Rudder* 82 (Dec. 1966), 19-20.

National Trust for Historic Preservation. *Wooden Shipbuilding & Small Craft Preservation.* Washington, D.C.: The Preservation Press, 1976.

Rabl, S.S. "Work Boats of the Chesapeake Bay." *Motor Boat* 22 (25 Oct. 1925), 10-3.

Scott, Stuart S. "Commercial Craft of the Chesapeake Region." *Motor Boat* 10 (Apr. 1913), 9-13.

Tilp, Frederick. *The Chesapeake Bay of Yore - Mainly About Rowing & Sailing Craft.* Alexandria,VA: Frederick Tilp, 1982.

_____. *This Was Potomac River.* Alexandria, VA: Frederick Tilp, 1987.

Wilson, Thomas. "Work Boats of the Chesapeake." *Motor Boat* 8 (Apr. 1910), 21-7.

Log-Built Boats

Armstrong, Kalani. "The Chesapeake Bay Canoe, from Forest to Flood." *The Rudder* 7 (Apr. 1896), 126-8; 192.

Brewington, M.V. *Chesapeake Bay Log Canoes and Bugeyes.* Cambridge, MD: Cornell Maritime Press, 1963.

_____. "Chesapeake Bay Log Canoes." In Clark, Charles B., *The Eastern Shore of Maryland and Virginia.* New York: Lewis Historical Publishing Co., 1950.

"The Buckeye." *Forest and Stream* 22 (14 Feb. 1884), 234-7.

Burgess, Robert H. "Carving of a Log Canoe." *National Fisherman* 52 (Jul. 1971), 34-5.

_____. "Dugout Log Canoes." *Chronicles of St. Mary's* 15 (Jan. 1967), 1-8.

_____. "Passage Home." *Chesapeake Skipper* 10 (Jun. 1952), 21-2; 38-43.

Chamberlain, Gloria. "Chesapeake Celebrity." *Chesapeake Bay Magazine* 19 (May 1989), 60-5.

Chambliss, Peter C. "The Bugeye of the Chesapeake." *In Sailing Craft*. Ed. Edwin J. Schoettle. New York: MacMillan Co., 1937, 198-215.

Chapman, S. Vannort. "The Chesapeake Bay Log Canoe of the Eastern Shore of Maryland." Manuscript, Maryland Historical Society, 1940.

Chowning, Larry S. "The Building of a Log Canoe Recalls Chesapeake's Past." *National Fisherman* 64 (Sept. 1983), 56-7.

Coe, Charles H. "The Chesapeake Canoe." *Motor Boat* 19 (25 Aug. 1922), 5-6.

Davis, William A. "The Chesapeake Bay Canoe: Its Evolution From the Dugout." *The Rudder* 21 (Apr. 1909), 350-5.

Earle, John G. "The Bugeye 'Triumph'." *Yachting* 55 (Feb. 1934), 81.

_____. "The Chesapeake Bay Log Canoe 'Magic'." *Yachting* 55 (Jan. 1934), 37-8.

Frye, John. "Chesapeake Log Canoe." *Boating* 19 (May 1966), 78-81.

Gardner, John. "New Log Canoes Being Built on the Chesapeake." *National Fisherman* 52 (May 1971), 12B-13B.

Green, William H. "History of Chesapeake Bay Log Canoes." *St. Michaels Comet*, 26 Jun. 1936.

_____. "Historical Facts About Chesapeake Canoes." *Star Democrat* [Easton], 16 Sep. 1932.

_____. " 'Mary Rider' The Story of a Chesapeake Bay Log Canoe." *Star Democrat* [Easton], 18 May 1962.

Hopkins, F. Snowden. "The Chesapeake's Old Log Canoes." *Sun* [Baltimore], 10 Jul. 1932.

Kaiser, F.F. "Century-Old Log Canoe Stirs Memories of Ex-Owner." *National Fisherman* 58 (Feb. 1978), 12C-13C.

_____. "Out to Pasture . . . A Chesapeake Racing Log Canoe Goes Day Sailing." *Motorboating* 95 (Jan. 1955), 76-80.

Kenealy, A.J. "The 'Cunners' of Chesapeake Bay." *Outing* (May 1900), 148-51.

Kenny, N.T. "The Bay Canoes Come Back." *The Rudder* 53 (Oct. 1937), 23.

_____. "How to Build a Log Canoe." *Sun* [Baltimore], 16 May 1948.

Lambdin, Robert D. "Shipbuilding on the Chesapeake: Recollections of Robert Dawson Lambdin." *Maryland Historical Magazine* 36 (Jun. 1941), 171-83.

Lavish, Alexander and George, Surgent. *Early Chesapeake Single-Log Canoes*. Solomons, MD: Calvert Marine Museum.

Leiber, William C. "The Buckeye." *The Rudder* 13 (May 1902), 245.

Miles River Yacht Club. *The Chesapeake Bay Log Sailing Canoe*. Easton, MD: n.p., 1933.

Peffer, Randall. "Cut and Look - Building a Chesapeake Bay Sailing Log Canoe." *WoodenBoat* 1 (1975), 27-33.

Phipps, William R. "Chesapeake Bay Log Canoes." *Chronicles of St. Mary's* 2 (Mar. 1963), 16-31.

Reppert, Ralph. "How to Build A Log Canoe." *Sun* [Baltimore], 30 Jul. 1972.

Scott, Stuart S. "The Bugeyes of the Chesapeake." *Motorboating* 8 (Nov. 1911), 7-10.

_____. "The Chesapeake Bay Bugeye." *Yachting* 23 (Mar. 1918), 138-40.

_____. "The Log Boats of the Chesapeake Bay." *The Rudder* 33 (Apr. 1917), 281-5.

Steinlein, Eric J. "The Chesapeake Bugeye." *Sun* [Baltimore], 3 Dec. 1972.

_____. "Log Canoes: Swift and Versatile." *Sun* [Baltimore], 30 Jul. 1972.

Valliant, E.T. "Chesapeake Racing Canoes." *The Rudder* 17 (Jul. 1906), 457-60.

Van Engel, W.A. "The Blue Crab and its Fishery in Chesapeake Bay - Part 2 - Types of Gear for Hard Crab Fishing." *Commercial Fisheries Review* 24 (Sept. 1962), 1-10.

Vaughan, Roger. "Or Else You Get Wet - Racing Log Canoes on the Chesapeake." *Nautical Quarterly* 22 (1983), 6-17.

Wallace, Adam. *The Parson of the Islands*. Philadelphia: Methodist Home Journal, 1872.

Warner, William W. "Winter 'Drudging' Lifts Crabs from the Chesapeake Mud." *Smithsonian* (Feb. 1976), 83-9.

Wiley, Ralph A. "'Spreets' on the Eastern Shore." *Yachting* 59 (Mar. 1936), 40-1.

Round-Bilge Boats

Burgess, Robert H. "The Yankee Skiff." *National Fisherman* 44 (Nov. 1963), 8.

Frye, John. *The Men all Singing - The Story of Menhaden Fishing*. Virginia Beach, VA: The Donning Company, 1978.

_____ ."The Menhaden Fleets of the Bay." *Sun* [Baltimore], 16 Jun 1974.

Gardner, John. "Building the Yankee Skiff." *National Fisherman* 66 (Aug. 1985), 60-2.

_____ . "Capable Yankee Skiff Even Adapts to Power." *National Fisherman* 66 (Jul. 1985), 44-5.

Greer, Robert L. "The Menhaden Industry of the Atlantic Coast." *Report of the Commissioner of Fisheries*. Washington, D.C.: GPO, 1914.

Guthorn, Peter J. *The Sea Bright Skiff and Other Jersey Shore Boats*. New Brunswick, NJ: Rutgers University Press, 1971.

Kochiss, John M. *Oystering From New York to Boston*. Middletown, CT: Wesleyan University Press, 1974.

V-Bottom Boats

Bauers, Bob. "The Life of a Hooper Island Boat." *Chesapeake Bay Magazine* 12 (May 1982), 36-8.

Beitzell, Edwin W. *Life on the Potomac*. Abell, MD: Edwin Beitzell, 1968.

_____ ."Potomac River 'Dory' Sails Again." *Chronicles of St. Mary's* 18 (Sept. 1970), 467-8.

Byron, Gilbert. "Bateau-Bateaux . . . Whence to the Chesapeake." *Chesapeake Bay Magazine* 18 (Mar. 1989), 32-3.

Burgess, Robert H. "Trade Wind on Rock Creek." *Chesapeake Bay Magazine* 14 (Dec. 1984), 20-2.

Chapelle, Howard I. *Chesapeake Bay Crabbing Skiffs*. St. Michaels, MD: Chesapeake Bay Maritime Museum, 1979.

_____ . *Notes on Chesapeake Bay Skipjacks*. St. Michaels, MD: Chesapeake Bay Maritime Museum, 1981.

_____ ."Practical Fishing Launches II." *Boats* 51 (Jul. 1954), 31-3.

Chowning, Larry S. *Barcat Skipper*. Centreville, MD: Tidewater Publishers, 1983.

_____ . "From Draketails to Potpie Sterns Chesapeake Watermen Appreciate a Nicely Shaped Rear End." *National Fisherman* 65 (Yearbook 1985), 78-80.

Dodge, Horace E. "Mass Production for Boats." *Motorboating* 45 (Feb. 1930), 106-7.

Gillmer, Thomas C. *Working Watercraft*. Camden, ME: International Marine Publishing Co., 1972.

Gregory, Joseph F. *"Deadrise Is From Here . . . to Yonder"*. Yorktown, VA: Skipjack Publications, 1987.

Hall, Christopher. "The Restoration of the *Stanley Norman*." *WoodenBoat* 35 (Jul./Aug. 1980), 62-7.

Horton, Tom. "The Greatest Crab Scraper of Them All." *Sun* [Baltimore], 21 Aug. 1988.

Kofoed, V. Beckwith. "How Boats are Manufactured Today." *Motorboating* 37 (Feb. 1926), 4-8.

Lang, Varley. *Follow the Water*. Winston Salem, NC: John F. Blair Publishers, 1961.

Lankford, Ben Jr. "Chesapeake Bay Oyster, Crab and Clam Boats." *Nautical Research Journal* 14 (Summer 1967), 43-62.

_____ . "*Metunga* of the Chesapeake." *Nautical Research Journal* 13 (Winter 1965), 113-20.

Lesher, Ronald E. Jr. "The Hooper Island Draketail." *The Weather Gauge* 24 (Spring 1988), 19-22.

Redmond, Steve. "Chesapeake Crabbing Skiffs." *WoodenBoat* 69 (Mar./Apr. 1986), 100-3.

Reppert, Ralph. "A Day with the Oyster Fleet." *Sun* [Baltimore], 20 Feb. 1972.

Simpson, Christopher. "Scraping 'Peelers' from Chesapeake Bay." *National Fisherman* 68 (May 1987), 22-4.

Steinlein, Eric. "Skipjacks of the Chesapeake." *Sun* [Baltimore], 8 Apr. 1973.

Stevens, Hugh D. "Of Sails & Oars & Yesterday. The Chesapeake Bay Crabbing Skiff." *Virginia Wildlife* 50 (Feb. 1989), 4-7.

Sucher, Harry V. *Simplified Boatbuilding: The V-Bottom Boat*. New York: W.W. Norton and Co., 1974.

Tawes, William I. *God, Man, Salt Water and the Eastern Shore*. Cambridge, MD: Tidewater Publishers, 1977.

Warner, William W. *Beautiful Swimmers*. Boston, MA: Little, Brown and Co., 1976.

Flat-Bottom Boats

Chapelle, Howard I. *The Migrations of an American Boat Type*. Contributions from the Museum of History and Technology Paper 25. United States National Museum Bulletin 228. Washington, D.C: Smithsonian Institution, 1963.

"Culler Builds a Sharptown Barge." *National Fisherman* 49.3(1968).

Emmett, J.A. "Workhorse of the Chesapeake: The Oyster Push Boats." *Yachting* 75 (Mar. 1944), 40.

Steward, Robert M. "How to build a Sharptown Barge." *The Rudder* 68 (Nov. 1952), 26-8.

_____. "Sharptown Barge." *The Rudder* 64 (Sept. 1948), 36.

Wooten, Orlando. "Riverman in Sharptown Recalls Golden Days of Fishing, Hunting." *Sunday Times* [Salisbury], 29 Apr. 1973.

Gunning Boats

Badger, Curtis J. "Classic Bay Duck Boats." *Chesapeake Bay Magazine* 19 (Nov. 1989), 30-3.

_____. "Classic Gunning Boats." *The Talbot Banner* [Easton], 10-16 May 1989.

_____. "Old-Time Duck Boats," *American Hunter* 16 (Jul. 1988), 32-5.

Blogg, Percy T. *There Are No Dull Dark Days*. Baltimore, MD: H.G. Roebuck and Son, 1944.

Camp, Raymond R. *Duck Boats, Blinds, Decoys and Eastern Seaboard Waterfowling*. New York: Alfred A. Knopf, 1952.

Crosby, W.F. "How to Build a Sinkboat." *The Rudder* 68 (Oct. 1932), 22-3.

Dale, Orton G. "Barnegat Bay Sneak Boxes." *Sailing Craft*. Ed. Edwin J. Schoettle. New York: MacMillan Co., 1942.

Grinnell George B. *American Duck Shooting*. New York: Forest and Stream Publishing Co., 1901.

Guthorn, Peter J. *The Sea Bright Skiff and other Jersey Shore Boats*. New Brunswick, NJ: Rutgers University Press, 1971.

Kimball, David & Jim. *The Market Hunter*. Minneapolis, MN: Dillon Press Inc., 1969.

Michael, H. Osborne. "The Bushwack Boat." *Motorboat* 25 (25 Apr. 1928), 14-6.

Miller, Stephen M. *Early American Waterfowling 1700s-1930*. Piscataway, NY: New Century Publisher, 1986.

Redmond, Steve. "The Versatile Sneakbox." *WoodenBoat* 61 (Nov./Dec.1984), 124-6.

Stark, Eric L. "The Barnegat Bay Sneakbox." *Woodenboat* 47 (Jul./Aug. 1982), 102-7.

Scrivanich, Skip. "They Bushwhack for Canvasback." *Maryland* 7 (Autumn 1974), 10-3.

Sullivan, C. John, Jr. *Waterfowling - The Upper Chesapeake's Legacy*. Fallston, MD: Maplehurst Publishers, 1987.

Walsh, Harry M. *The Outlaw Gunner*. Cambridge, MD: Tidewater Publishers, 1971.

One-Design Boats

"The Albatross Class." *Yachting* 60 (Oct. 1936), 72.

Bedford, F.T. "One Design." *Sailing Craft*. Ed. Edwin J. Schoettle. New York: MacMillan Co., 1937.

Blanchard, Fessenden S. *The Sailboat Classes of North America*. Garden City, NY: Doubleday & Co., 1963.

Brett, Dare. "A Young Brother of the Stars for Chesapeake Bay." *Yachting* 51 (Mar. 1932), 90.

Burchard, Hank. "Bay Built: A Man and a Boat." *Washington Post* n.d.

Elder, G.W. and Ratney, Ernest. "The International Star Class." In *Sailing Craft*. Ed. Edwin J. Schoettle. NewYork: MacMillan Co., 1937.

Frye, John. "You're Probably Too Young to Know the Chesapeake 20." *Soundings* (Oct. 1983), p.4, Sec. II

Hartge, Laurence. "A Memorable Weekend." *Chesapeake Bay Magazine* 18 (Feb. 1989), 59-61.

Holmes, Bill. "Built to Win." *WoodenBoat* 27 (Mar./Apr. 1979), 94-5.

Hosmer, E. Fletcher, ed. *A Look at the Comet 1932-1982*. Surf City NJ: CCYRA, 1982.

Kenny, N.T. "The Star Class." *The Rudder* 67 (June, 1951), 28-9.

Lambourne, Malcom D. Jr. "Born and Bred on the Chesapeake." *Yachting* 72 (Nov. 1942), 26-8.

_____. "The Penguins Get Around." *Yachting* 81 (May 1947), 64; 118-20.

Lucke, Charles E. Jr. "The Stars Come of Age." *Yachting* 51 (Jan. 1932), 75-6.

Mathews, William B. Jr. "The St. Michaels Sailing Scow." *Miles River Yacht Club Yearbook* 1981.

Meara, Robert A. "A Sailboat Built for Two." *Sun* [Baltimore], 23 May 1954.

Miller, Robert R. and Pearre, Aubrey. *Fifteenth Anniversary Record of the Chesapeake Bay Fleet ISCYRA.* Baltimore: Members of the Chesapeake Bay Fleet, 1938.

"The Original Hampton One Design." *The Mariners' Museum Journal* (Winter 1980).

Phillips - Birt, Douglas. *The History of Yachting.* New York: Stein and Day, 1974.

Reinke, Tom. "The Rising Star - A Classic Keelboat Turns 75." *Small Boat Journal* 52 (Dec./Jan. 1987), 41-3.

"Renowned Boat Designer Dies." *Star Democrat* [Easton], 6 Jan. 1971.

Robinson, Bill. *The World of Yachting.* New York: Random House, 1966.

Slane, James F. "Johnson's 'Comet' The Development of a Popular One-Design Class." *Yachting* 55 (Mar. 1934), 63.

Smith, Rufus G. "The Penguin A Smart Sailing Dingy." *Yachting* 67 (May 1940), 61-2.

Taylor, William H. and Rosenfeld, Stanley. *The Story of American Yachting.* New York: Appleton - Century - Crafts, 1958.

Trimble, Nancy. "One Design." *Soundings* (May 1982), n.p.

Wallace, William N. *The MacMillan Book of Boating.* New York: MacMillan Co., 1964.

Webb, George. *50th Anniversary of the Hampton Class.* n.p., n.p. 1974.

Smith, S. Calhoun. *Ice Boating.* Princeton, NJ: D. Van Nostrand Co., 1962.

Miscellaneous Boats

Ruge, Raymond A. "The History and Development of the Iceboat Part 1." *WoodenBoat* 38 (Jan./Feb. 1981), 64-70.

_____. "The History and Development of the Iceboat Part 2." *WoodenBoat* 39 (Mar./Apr. 1981), 88-95.

Schoettle, Edwin J. "Ice Boating." *Sailing Craft.* Ed. Edwin J. Schoettle. New York: MacMillan Co., 1937.